WHY
ANIMAL
EXPERIMENTS
MUST
STOP

Books by the same author include:

The Medicine Men (1975)
Paper Doctors (1976)
Everything You Want to Know About Ageing (1976)
Stress Control (1978)
The Home Pharmacy (1980)
Aspirin or Ambulance (1980)
Face Values (1981)
Guilt (1982)
The Good Medicine Guide (1982)
Stress and Your Stomach (1983)
Bodypower (1983)
Thomas Winsden's Cricketing Almanack (1983)
A Guide to Child Health (1984)
An A to Z of Women's Problems (1984)
Bodysense (1984)
Taking Care of Your Skin (1984)
Diary of a Cricket Lover (1984)
Life Without Tranquillisers (1985)
High Blood Pressure (1985)
Diabetes (1985)
Arthritis (1985)
Eczema and Dermatitis (1985)
The Story of Medicine (1985)
Natural Pain Control (1986)
Mindpower (1986)
Addicts and Addictions (1986)
Dr Vernon Coleman's Guide to Alternative Medicine (1988)
Stress Management Techniques (1988)
Overcoming Stress (1988)
Know Yourself (1988)
The Health Scandal (1988)
The 20 Minute Health Check (1989)
Sex for Everyone (1989)
Mind Over Body (1989)
Eat Green Lose Weight (1990)
Toxic Stress (1991)
Why Animal Experiments Must Stop (1991)
The Drugs Myth (1992)
Arthritis (1993)
Backache (1993)
Stress and Relaxation (1993)
Complete Guide to Good Sex (1993)
Why Doctors Do More Harm Than Good (1993)

Novels
The Village Cricket Tour (1990)
The Bilbury Chronicles (1992)
Bilbury Grange (1993)
Mrs Caldicot's Cabbage War (1993)
The Man Who Inherited a Golf Club (1993)

Writing as Edward Vernon
Practice Makes Perfect (novel, 1977)
Practise What You Preach (novel, 1978)
Getting into Practice (novel, 1979)
Aphrodisiacs—An Owner's Manual (1983)
The Complete Guide to Life (1984)

As Marc Charbonnier
Tunnel (novel, 1980)

With Dr Alan C. Turin
No More Headaches (1981)

With Alice
Alice's Diary (1989)
Alice's Adventures (1992)

WHY ANIMAL EXPERIMENTS MUST STOP

AND HOW YOU CAN HELP STOP THEM

Vernon Coleman

EUROPEAN
MEDICAL
JOURNAL

First published in 1991 by Green Print
Reprinted in 1994 by the European Medical Journal, Lynmouth, Devon
EX35 6EE, United Kingdom

The right of Vernon Coleman to be identified as author of this work has
been asserted in accordance with the Copyright, Designs and Patents Act
1988

ISBN 0 9521492 1 4

All royalties and proceeds from the sale of this book go to help the
campaign against animal experiments

Printed and bound by Biddles Ltd, Guildford, England

What the papers say about Dr Vernon Coleman

Dr Vernon Coleman's books have been translated into 14 languages and sold in just about every country in the world. Here are some comments about him and his previous books from the British Press:

'Britain's leading health care campaigner' – *The Sun* 'The sharpest mind in medical journalism' – *The Star* 'Dr Coleman writes with more sense than bias' – *Daily Express* 'GP turned author whose concern is providing the layman with good advice on a variety of subjects' – *Yorkshire Post* 'Dr Coleman has in recent years challenged accepted ideas about everything from beauty products to more strictly medical matters' – *The Scotsman* 'Outspoken and alert observer' – *Sunday Express* 'He is a fluent writer, all commonsense and no nonsense' – *Health Services Management* 'GP turned columnist whose writings send the medical establishment into a flat spin' – *Express and Star* 'The most influential medical writer in Britain. There can be little doubt that Vernon Coleman is the people's doctor' – *Devon Life* 'The medical expert you can't ignore' – *Sunday Independent* 'The doctor who dares to speak his mind' – *Oxford Mail* 'Man with a mission' – *Morning News* 'Dr Coleman is more illuminating than the proverbial lady with the lamp' – *Company Magazine* 'One of the country's leading medical authors' – *The Times* 'Dr Coleman has the gift of being able to sweeten the bitter pill of knowledge . . . presenting revolutionary concepts in words everyone can understand' – *Evening Telegraph* 'Refreshingly sensible' – *Spectator* 'Dr Coleman gains in stature with successive books' – *Coventry Evening Telegraph* 'He has a racy and lucid style and he successfully combines the gifts of a journalist and of a perspicacious reader' – *Good Housekeeping* 'A writer with the common touch . . . his humour masks deep thinking about subjects which interest him' – *Yorkshire Evening Post* 'The patient's champion. The doctor with the common touch' – *Birmingham Post* 'Dr Coleman has a string of successful titles to his credit and the outspoken, sometimes controversial and often humorous attitude he brings to writing has done much to enhance his reputation' – *Warwickshire and Worcestershire Life* 'Clear and helpful' – *The Guardian* 'Vernon Coleman is a leading medical authority and known to millions through his writing, broadcasting and best selling books' – *Womans Own* 'His message is important' – *The Economist* 'It is always stimulating to read Vernon Coleman' – *The Liberator* 'Its impossible not to be impressed' – *Western Daily Press* 'A persuasive writer whose arguments, based on research and experience, are sound' – *Nursing Standard* 'Refreshingly forthright' – *Liverpool Daily Post* 'You can always rely on Dr Coleman for frank advice' – *Over 21* 'Not a man to pull his punches' – *Sunday Mercury* 'Vernon Coleman has written many highly informative books for the general public' – *True Magazine* 'Dr Coleman's study will do much to enlighten not only the medical profession but also every man' – *Books and Bookmen* 'His book 'Bodypower' is one of the most sensible treatises on personal survival that has every been published' – *Yorkshire Evening Post* 'His wise handbook 'Stress

Control' is a bible for those who wish to understand and combat stress' – *Company* 'Britain's leading medical author' – *The Stars and Stripes* 'Dr Coleman is crusading for a more complete awareness of what is good and bad for our bodies. In the course of that he has made many friends and some powerful enemies' – *Western Morning News* 'His advice is practical and readable' – *The Northern Echo* 'His advice is optimistic and enthusiastic' – *British Medical Journal* 'Dr Coleman is one medic who doesn't beat about the bush' – *New Woman* 'Dr Coleman speaks openly and reassuringly' – *Oxford Times* 'Hurrah, then for Dr Vernon Coleman' – *Sheffield Telegraph* 'One of Britain's leading experts' – *Slimmer Magazine* 'Acknowledged authority' – *The Observer* 'Dr Coleman has a maverick reputation for his writings on the tactics of the drug industry and his questioning of some established medical treatments' – *Sunday Times* 'Merciless' – *Evening Times, Glasgow* 'His advice is clear and commonsensible' – *Evening News* 'What he says . . . is true' – *Punch* 'He is keenly aware of the social dimensions of medical practice' – *Times Literary Supplement* 'Vernon Coleman has a common sense and practical approach to providing answers for real people living lives they can't totally control' – *Weight Watchers* 'Dr Coleman lays about him with an uncompromising verbal scalpel, dipped in vitriol, against all sorts of sacred cows' – *Exeter Express and Echo* 'Dr Coleman has thoroughly and unerringly investigated and published the workings of the health service' – *Fitness Magazine* 'Dr Coleman . . . has a string of medical bestsellers to his name' – *Health Service Journal* 'Has done more to undermine the establishment's use of Aids to promote fear and insecurity . . . than the whole of the left' – *Living Marxism* 'Coleman presses on persuasively (and) provides thought provoking ideas' – *Conservative Newspaper* 'Dr Coleman manages to present complex technical arguments in a simple and understandable way . . . he argues very cogently and convincingly . . . what he says is valid and needs to be said' – *Nursing Times* 'A godsend' – *Daily Telegraph*

To Sue, to Alice and Tom and to the unloved victims of science.

'I know not, that by living dissections any discovery has been made by which a single malady is more easily cured.'

SAMUEL JOHNSON (1709–84)

CONTENTS

PREFACE

I HAVE BEEN OPPOSED TO VIVISECTION for many years; not just because it is unbelievably barbaric and unforgiveably cruel but also because it is worthless, wasteful, inaccurate, uninformative and dangerously misleading.

The cruelty is indefensible and an affront to human dignity, but in a desperate attempt to justify their evil practices many vivisectors still claim that what they do helps save human lives. They are lying. The truth is that *animal experiments kill people* and animal researchers are responsible for the deaths of thousands of men, women and children every year; they are also directly responsible for a massive amount of human suffering.

The callous self-interest of vivisectors leads directly to the development and marketing of unsafe drugs and medical practices; there is without a shadow of doubt a conspiracy between the medical profession and the drugs industry to defend and protect a practice which has as much relevance to science as alchemy.

A future, more enlightened world will see vivisection as one of the more obscene and inexplicable practices of our age; it is our equivalent of slavery and cruel colonialism and those who fail to condemn it loudly will be branded as being as guilty as the vivisectors themselves by tomorrow's generations.

Animal experiments are done for personal and commercial gain by people who are driven by greed and vanity. But although the vivisectors may be cruel, unthinking and unimaginative,

1

they are not entirely without cunning. They realize that their best chance of continuing with their work is to persuade the public that the work they do does have a value. And so they lie. And because they are backed by huge international corporations which are as frightened as they are wealthy, the lies are presented in a convincing and polished way. They terrorize and blackmail ordinary citizens by warning them that if animal experiments are stopped their children will die. It is crude and dishonest but it is often effective.

The only way to defeat these lies is to tell the truth in simple but convincing detail. And that is why I have written this book.

Together we can stop vivisection. And we will.

Vernon Coleman
Devon, 1991

1 THE BASIC FACTS

LET US FIRST LOOK AT what goes on in the world's laboratories – the number of animals involved – where the animals come from – where the money comes from – and examples of the sort of experiments performed in modern laboratories.

How many animals are involved?

It is impossible to say precisely how many animals are abused, tortured, maimed and killed every year in the name of science. It is impossible because many scientists, well aware of the fact that what they do is worthless and unpopular, are secretive and refuse to disclose details of the animals they have used.

But, using the figures that are available, it is possible to make fairly accurate estimates. In America academic researchers use between 17 and 22 million animals a year, while the cosmetics industry there uses another million or so. In Britain experimental scientists use between 3 and 4 million animals a year. Altogether the total number of animals used around the world is probably somewhere in the region of 250 million.

Or, to put the figures in a slightly more manageable way, animal experimenters use around 100,000-125,000 animals an hour.

Where do the animals come from?

The demand for animals to cut up and kill is massive and so there are, inevitably, a number of people who earn their living by providing laboratories with the livestock they need. Supplying live animals is big business these days.

But where do the suppliers get the animals from?

Many of the animals are specially bred on animal farms where sophisticated techniques may be used to ensure that researchers get what they want. Some animals come from zoos (when they have a surplus of some species available), some are retired from other activities (ex-racing greyhounds are popular with researchers) and some are captured in the wild.

It is this last method that arouses most indignation among environmental pressure groups, for some animals are captured in such vast quantities that whole species are threatened with extinction.

Way back in 1972 E. G. Hartley of the National Institute for Medical Research in London warned that 'in certain areas of India in which the rhesus (monkey) population was high some years ago few are now to be found'. Hartley went on to say that 'No one can deny that some effect on the conservation of certain primate species has been caused by the large number of primates captured annually for biochemical research purposes'.

Things have not changed much – if at all – since then. One British-based animal supplier recently imported 10,000 monkeys

4

into Britain over a four year period. The animals had been trapped, in the wild, in Malaysia, Indonesia and the Philippines. After enduring journeys which can be long, difficult and desperately uncomfortable such animals must then exchange their freedom for laboratory cages and their natural lifestyle for boredom and pain.

The constant fear of many animal lovers is that their family pet may one day end up in a laboratory and there is evidence to show that such fears are well-founded. According to Dr James B. Wyngaarden of America's National Institutes of Health, writing in the *Journal of the American Medical Association* recently, around 200,000 cats and dogs are picked up off the streets in America every year — and then handed over to vivisectors to be used in experiments.

Where does the money come from?

It is impossible to estimate accurately how much money is spent on animal experiments, partly because there is so much secrecy surrounding everything these researchers do and partly because the money comes from so many different directions.

But the total sum involved is huge and despite occasional public pleas of poverty from individual researchers there is little doubt that the vivisection business is financially strong and unlikely to wither for lack of funds.

Most of the cash comes from three major sources: government, industry and charitable organizations. Between them the money men dish out vast quantities of money contributed by taxpayers, shareholders and people who have put money into collecting tins in the belief that they are helping to fight cancer, heart disease or some other disabling disease.

Most of the money contributed through governments is channelled into animal research via three specific departments.

First, and most obviously, a lot of money comes from

5

departments or officially funded organizations which exist to help scientists.

Much of this money is available for 'pure' research which does not have to have any obvious, immediate, practical uses. Lots of it goes into institutions where it helps to pay for some of the world's most entirely useless research. It is fairly well accepted these days that scientists working in animal research can be pretty second rate, but many of these scientists have got very good at filling in grant application forms.

The next route that government money takes is usually through the world of education. Fairly huge quantities of cash are made available so that students can experiment on live frogs, rabbits and cats – invariably repeating experiments which have been performed a thousand times before. But the really big money goes to postgraduate departments in universities where vast armies of white-coated pseudo-scientists are constantly searching for new ways to extract scientific papers from rats, cats, dogs and monkeys.

Finally, a considerable amount of money arrives in the hands of animal experimenters via defence and war ministries.

When money come from this direction the amount of secrecy involved – always vast – becomes even greater. The fears and guilt-driven paranoia of ordinary animal experimenters are compounded by the deep-rooted fears and very special paranoias of the military establishment.

The largest portion of the money that is spent by industry on animal experiments comes from drug companies (making products for doctors to prescribe and for customers to buy over the chemist's counter) and cosmetic companies; together they spend a fortune on testing and investigating new ingredients and potential new products. But the involvement of industry is not limited to these two areas; companies which make products as varied as food additives, industrial and agricultural chemicals and household cleansers all do an enormous amount of testing on animals too.

Charities are the third major source of money for animal experiments. Funded by millions of small, individual donations from people who are attracted by the brash promises to conquer disease and find 'wonder cures', medical charities rely heavily on the fact that although most of us realize that it is our bad habits which make us ill we still like the idea of someone finding a magical cure that will absolve us from taking any real, practical responsibility for our health.

In the end the route the money takes on its way to the animal experimenters is almost irrelevant. Whether the cash is paid over by a government department, a medical charity or a major international company, the real source of the money is not some anonymous accountant or bureaucrat: the money that pays for animal experiments comes from your wallet or purse.

You are paying for animal experiments when you pay your taxes, when you give money to a big medical charity or when you buy any product made by a company which has animal experimenters on its payroll.

You are entitled to know what animal experimenters are doing with the money they get and you are entitled to have a say in stopping them doing it, for the very good but simple reason that you are helping to pay the bills.

As you read on, just remember that you have helped to pay for virtually every experiment described in this book; you have helped buy the animals, you have helped equip the laboratories and you have paid the fat salaries of the white-coated men and women who have dreamt up and then performed the experiments.

I hope that fact makes you as angry as it makes me.

A catalogue of misery

It is difficult to know where to start – or stop – when describing

7

the sort of experiments conducted by vivisectionists. I have a filing cabinet filled with research papers from universities and institutions all over the world and there seems no end to the variety of indignities that researchers can think up for the animals in their power.

In the end I decided merely to list very brief summaries of a handful of experiments that have been done in recent years. These are fairly typical examples – neither more nor less horrifying than thousands of other experiments conducted daily around the world. I have deliberately chosen not to comment too much on any of these experiments, since my comments and criticisms appear later in the book. I will add, however, that I have had to bowdlerize some of the experiments I have described; just reading the original, unexpurgated papers describing some of these experiments made me feel so ill and so angry that I repeatedly had to stop work while preparing this section.

Three final points are worth making.

First, while you read about these experiments try to remember that every hour of every day between 100,000 and 125,000 similar experiments are going on in laboratories around the world.

Second, if you want to know what experiments are being conducted at universities or other institutions near to where you live just get in touch with your nearest anti-vivisection society.

Third, do not forget that most (if not all) of these experiments were conducted on your behalf and with your money.

1. British researchers blinded two domestic tabby kittens by sewing up their conjunctivae and eyelids. The kittens were then placed in a special holder and horseradish peroxidase was injected into their brains. The kittens were then killed.

2. Three researchers conducted an experiment in which female hamsters were distracted with sunflower seeds so that their babies could be removed from the nest a few hours after birth.

8

Under 'hypothermic anaesthesia' the baby hamsters had their left eyes removed. They were then returned to their mothers. The scientists used fifty-nine golden hamsters in this experiment and removed the left eyes from 'about half'.

3. At the United States Armed Forces Radiobiology Research Institute in Bethesda, Maryland, a researcher spent nine weeks forcing thirty-nine monkeys to run on a cylindrical treadmill known as an 'activity wheel'. If the monkeys failed to run for long enough they got an electric shock.

4. Researchers funded by the UK Medical Research Council gave ferrets a drug that made them vomit at between half minute and five minute intervals. The researchers gave the ferrets another drug and concluded that under some circumstances the ferrets did not stand up to vomit and that under the influence of the second drug their vomiting was less forceful.

5. Three adult female cats were selected for a Welsh laboratory experiment because they were very docile. Wires from the cats' eyes were connected to a device held in place on the cats' skulls with self-tapping stainless steel screws. The cats were kept awake and their eye movements measured while their bodies were rotated and tilted and stimulated in other ways.

6. American researchers separated young kittens from their mothers to see what effect this had. At the end of the experiment the scientists concluded that separated kittens cried more than those who remained in close contact with their mothers. The scientists added that the crying seemed to denote stress.

7. Two eminent researchers working in America conducted a series of experiments designed to make baby monkeys depressed. To begin with they created a cloth, surrogate mother which could be triggered to blow out high pressure compressed

9

air. When the baby monkey went to give its fake mum a hug the researcher would press a button and try to blast the baby monkey away. However, this did not work and the baby monkey merely clung on tighter. The researchers then built a surrogate monster mother that was designed to rock so violently that the baby's 'head and teeth would rattle'. Again, the baby monkey just clung on tightly. The third monster had a wire frame built into its body. The frame was designed to throw the baby away from it. This worked to a certain extent – in that it did successfully separate the baby from its fake mother – but the baby monkey just picked itself up and went back to its fake mother immediately afterwards. In a final attempt to alienate, terrify and thus depress the baby monkey the researchers built a 'porcupine' mother from which, at the press of a remote switch, sharp brass spikes would leap out. Once again the experiment was a failure for although the baby monkey was upset by the spikes it simply waited until the spikes had been withdrawn before returning to its mother.

8. The same researchers also created a 'well of despair' for monkeys. They built a vertical chamber with stainless steel sides and a rounded bottom and put young monkeys in it for weeks at a time. On this occasion the two researchers were successful. The monkeys eventually sat huddled at the bottom of the chamber looking depressed.

9. Scottish scientists pushed fine polythene tubes into rats' brains. They then put balloons into the rats' brains and blew them up. They found that all the rats suffered brain damage but that the smaller balloons did not produce as much damage as the big balloons.

10. Four British research scientists surgically joined together 224 individual rats to make 112 sets of 'fake' siamese twins.

11. Rats' tails were immersed in hot water so that the experi-

10

menters could study pain in rats.

12. Ten beagle dogs were deliberately given stomach ulcers.

13. Balloons made from condoms were pushed into dogs' stomachs through metal tubes and then filled with water. During the experiment the dogs, which were hung in slings, were kept awake.

14. The livers, kidneys and lungs of Guernsey calves were deliberately damaged to see how this affected the way the animals responded to drugs. The researchers concluded that animals with damaged organs sometimes get more unpleasant side effects when they take drugs.

15. Six monkeys were given a drug so that they would develop Parkinson's disease. They were then given the drug which is commonly used to treat Parkinson's disease in humans. When the monkeys' symptoms improved they were killed.

16. Cuts were made in the bodies of pregnant rats and metal screws cooled in liquid nitrogen were held against the developing heads of the baby rats. The baby rats were later killed and their brains removed so that the amount of damage could be assessed.

17. Two researchers in London found that if they breathed heavily on ants as they came out of their nest early in the morning the ants panicked.

18. Three research workers shot around twenty monkeys just above the eye and then watched to see how long it took them to die. One monkey survived for over two and a half hours.

19. A psychologist removed a monkey's visual cortex and then kept the blinded monkey for six years so that he could study her behaviour.

20. Researchers have kept the brains of animals alive outside their bodies and have transplanted the heads of monkeys onto the bodies of other animals. Such experiments have taken place in a number of laboratories.

21. An American researcher gave a pair of rats a total of 15,000 electric shocks in seven and a half hours. Later the researcher heated the cage floor so that the rats inside jumped about, licking their feet, as the floor got hotter and hotter.

22. Researchers clipped the hair from forty beagle puppies. They then put kerosene-soaked gauze onto the beagles' naked bodies and set fire to the gauze.

23. In a series of experiments conducted in France, over thirty baboons were killed in forty miles an hour fake car crashes. A number of monkeys were killed when their skulls were hit with a hammering device. The experiments showed that animals would be endangered if they drove cars into walls at forty miles an hour.

24. In a Canadian experiment three polar bears were made to swim through a tank filled with crude oil and water. When the oil coated their fur the bears tried to lick themselves clean. They swallowed so much oil that they developed kidney failure and died. The conclusion was that polar bears should be kept away from oil slicks.

25. Two experimental scientists designed a drum rather like a tumbledrier for traumatizing alert, awake animals. The drum was made so that it turned over forty times a minute with the animal inside falling from one side to the other twice during each rotation. During a five minute experiment an animal inside the drum fell four hundred times. The animal's paws were taped together so that it could not break its own fall and interfere with the traumatizing process. Animals traumatized in the drum suffered broken teeth, concussion, bleeding and bruising of the liver.

2 | THE LIES THEY TELL

IN THEIR ATTEMPTS TO DEFEND the terrible things they do, animal researchers tell a lot of lies – here are some of the commonest, together with the real facts.

Lie number 1: *They say that animals are properly anaesthetized during painful or uncomfortable experiments.*

The evidence shows that this simply is not true. Approximately three quarters of all animal experiments are conducted without any anaesthetic at all and recent figures show that the number of experiments is going up. For example, one recent set of Home Office figures in Britain showed that during a twelve month period the number of experiments performed without anaesthetics on baboons went up by 11 per cent, the number of experiments without anaesthetics on rabbits went up by 20 per cent and the number of experiments done without anaesthetics on beagles went up by 15 per cent.

Even when anaesthetics are used the available evidence suggests that they are often inadequate. It is rare for a scientist experimenting on animals to have a properly trained anaesthetist present during a procedure and there is no doubt that many of the scientists who have licences to experiment on animals do not understand how anaesthetics need to be given. Anaesthesia is a complex, sophisticated speciality which it takes doctors years to master. As a result of ignorance many animals are paralysed but not anaesthetized – with the result that although they cannot move or cry out, they can still feel pain. Other animals are simply given inadequate quantities of anaesthetic.

The story of Wilhelm Feldberg, a researcher at the National Institute for Medical Research in London, helps demolish the myth that animals are always anaesthetized.

I first wrote about Feldberg several years ago after a reader of mine had brought his activities to my attention.

Feldberg studied medicine in Heidelberg, Munich and Berlin and in 1949 was appointed Head of the Division of Physiology and Pharmacology at the National Institute for Medical Research. It was there that many of his experiments were performed in the years that followed.

Looked at on paper Feldberg's list of qualifications and academic achievements was impressive. He was a medically qualified doctor, a Fellow of the Royal Society, a Fellow of the Royal College of Physicians and a Commander of the British Empire. Much of Feldberg's work was made possible by grants from the Medical Research Council.

A fairly typical scientific paper was published in the *British Journal of Pharmacology* in 1978 after Feldberg and a colleague performed a series of experiments on cats.

To begin with the experimenters implanted a tube into the brains of the cats. Then, when the cats had recovered from the anaesthetic, a mustard drug was injected straight down the tube into their brains. It was not difficult to imagine what happened next, but it may help if I quote directly from the paper that Feldberg and his colleague wrote:

> *Following these injections, shivering began within a minute or two and quickly became vigorous and widespread. The next effect was vocalization. It began with periods of miaowing which became more frequent and of longer duration and gradually the miaowing changed to growling and yelping. Later tachypnoea (rapid breathing), panting, salivation, piloerection (hair standing on end) and ear twitching were observed; later again, periods of intense excitation alternated with periods of a more restful condition. During the periods of excitation the cat would suddenly charge blindly ahead or jump up to or cling on to the side or the roof of the cage, the pupils being maximally dilated. The cats showed compulsive biting; care had to be taken to prevent them biting through the lead of the rectal probe (a thermometer had been tied into the cats' rectums) by offering them instead a pencil on which they could clamp their teeth and eventually gnaw through.*

If teenage youths had performed these experiments with stray cats they would have been locked up. Feldberg, who had discovered that if you stick mustard into the brain of a live, unanaesthetized cat it would pant, salivate, leap up and down, miaow and try to bite its way through anything in reach, was given buckets of cash to perform variations on the same experiment and write about it in scientific journals.

For example, in 1983 Feldberg (this time working with two new chums) published a scientific paper entitled 'Hyperglycaemia, a morphine like effect produced by naloxone in the cat'.

In order to write this scientific paper Feldberg started off by putting tubes into the brains of live cats. Once again he discovered that if you inject a substance into a cat's brain while it is still alive and conscious it gets physically upset. Feldberg reported that his cats shivered, miaowed, panted, salivated, retched, vomited and lost control of their bladders and bowels.

Feldberg did experiments like this for around thirty years, injecting a variety of chemicals into the brains of live, unanaesthetized cats. And he wrote a lot of scientific papers and became one of Britain's most honoured scientists.

Feldberg worked a lot with cats, but it was experiments on rabbits which brought about his downfall in the early summer of 1990 – just four months after he was awarded the Wellcome Gold Medal in Pharmacology by the British Pharmacological Society.

Just before Christmas 1989 two undercover operators finally persuaded Feldberg to allow them to take video and still photographs of him at work. Flattered by the attention he was getting (one of the investigators, Melody MacDonald, was a former fashion model) Feldberg agreed.

As a result of film which the investigators took just after Feldberg's eighty-ninth birthday, the Medical Research Council held an inquiry. The published report of the inquiry shows that according to the Medical Research Council Feldberg failed to ensure that four of the rabbits he used were sufficiently anaesthetized during experiments performed at the National Institute for Medical Research, in Mill Hill, London. The Medical Research Council's report describes the benefit likely to accrue from Feldberg's work as 'negligible' and admitted that 'applied to the methodology the word "crude" is not inappropriate'. They conclude that 'a number of animals perished for no discernible beneficial reason' and criticized the British Home Secretary for the fact that he 'failed to weigh adequately the likely benefit of the research against the likely adverse effects on the animals involved'.

In some ways Feldberg was probably unlucky. I very much doubt if he was the only scientist in Britain who was failing to anaesthetize laboratory animals properly. He certainly wasn't the only scientist doing research work of negligible value.

It's quite clear from this case history that it is a lie to say that animals which are experimented on are invariably and adequately anaesthetized. The truth is that most animals have no anaesthetic at all; and even when an anaesthetic is used the chances are high that it will be inadequate.

Lie number 2: *They say that the majority of scientists 'only' use mice and rats and that most of the people who protest about animal experiments only do so because they think that cats and dogs are involved.*

This time scientists (and their supporters) attempt to mislead the public in two quite separate ways.

First, they imply that rats and mice do not matter. This simply is not true, of course. The vast majority of those who disapprove of animal experiments disapprove of *all* animal experiments – it does not matter whether experiments involve cats, sheep, mice, dogs, gerbils, guinea pigs or frogs. The principles which are followed by those who oppose vivisection are identical whatever the creature.

Second, they lie when they suggest that experiments involving cats, dogs and primates are rare. The truth is that I doubt if there is a species known to us which has not been used in experiments by vivisectors. Monkeys, baboons and other primates are popular because it is easier for a scientist to argue that work done on a monkey is relevant to human beings than it is to make the same claim for work done on rats or mice. Rabbits are popular because their large eyes make a convenient test site for newly developed chemicals.

British experimenters use around 13,000 dogs a year and are particularly fond of beagles as experimental animals because

19

they are friendly, trusting and intelligent. Talk to a scientist who uses beagles and they will tell you that they like working with them because their confidence is easily won.

At one British university a zoology researcher 'obtained' two greater horseshoe bats (an endangered and protected species) and kept them for eighteen months in a plywood box. Each side of the box was 0.6 metres long and the walls were lined with plastic netting.

In laboratories all over the world research scientists are regularly experimenting on animals as small as hamsters, guinea pigs and gerbils or as large as pigs, sheep and horses. Some animals are specially bred for laboratories. Others are 'acquired' in dubious circumstances. Large or small, young or old, tame or wild, animals are tortured, watched and then killed. Name any species and I will name the experiment. You envisage the suffering and I will find evidence of an experiment far worse and far more obscene than anything you can think of.

Lie number 3: Researchers claim that the animals they use are well looked after. They say that all experimenters care deeply about the animals they use and that before, during and after experiments animals are treated with care and respect.

Sadly, the evidence shows that this is far from true.

Consider, for example, the case of eminent American psychologist Dr Edward Taub who for years conducted experiments in which the nerves controlling monkeys' arms were damaged. The alleged aim of the research work was to find information that would help human stroke victims, but doctors have been investigating stroke victims for decades and I can think of no reason why anyone should want to conduct such experiments on animals.

20

It was through the efforts of an undercover activist called Alexander Pacheco that Taub's research methods were brought to the public's attention. Pacheco reported that he saw one animal collapse through not being fed and that he was instructed to torment and frustrate the monkeys, which were often strapped into 'crucifix' type restraints, with their eyes blindfolded and their heads locked into vices. Bones had been broken and some monkeys had been so distressed that they appeared to have bitten off their own fingers. The cages in which the monkeys were kept were described as rusty and filthy dirty.

After taking photographs of the monkeys Pacheco brought a lawsuit against Taub, who was charged on seventeen separate counts of cruelty – one for each of the seventeen monkeys who were involved in the experiments. During the police raid which followed the lawsuit investigating officers discovered rubbish bins filled with the mutilated bodies of monkeys.

At his original trial Taub was fined a total of $3,000 for failing to provide veterinary care for six monkeys who were said to be in urgent need of treatment. The National Institutes of Health cancelled a large grant to the laboratory where Taub worked. Eventually, however, Taub managed to get the convictions overturned. One judge discounted physical damage and suffering as subjective and inadmissible. Another court overturned one conviction on the grounds that a state's anti-cruelty law could not be applied to a federally funded research project. Another court concluded that human beings had no legal standing to sue on behalf of monkeys. And Taub ended up by claiming that he was a martyr to science.

Taub is by no means the only researcher to have been accused of mistreating laboratory animals.

● In an experiment conducted by researchers in Pennsylvania baboons' heads were pushed violently to one side by a pneumatic ram. The aim was to investigate the effects of head injuries. The animals were supposed to have been anaesthetized

21

during the experiments but afterwards the United States Department of Agriculture charged the University of Pennsylvania with over twenty violations of the Animals Welfare Act. The researchers were accused of sneering and joking at the way the sad, braindamaged baboons moved after they had been injured.

● In London the Royal College of Surgeons was found guilty of causing unnecessary suffering to a laboratory monkey and fined £250 after the British Union for the Abolition of Vivisection brought a private prosecution, using evidence obtained during a raid on the College's research centre. A ten year old monkey was reported to have been found collapsed on the floor of her tiny, box type cell suffering from dehydration. The ruling was overturned after the Royal College of Surgeons appealed on what appeared to be legal grounds.

In most countries researchers can usually avoid prosecution by keeping their laboratories locked and by claiming that everything they do is part of an experiment (even the most unbelievable cruelty can be sanctioned legally if the researcher claims that the suffering was part of the experiment).

Even where attempts have been made to introduce legislation to protect laboratory animals there have been appalling delays. For example, a quarter of a century after a law was passed to control the use of animals in American research laboratories, and four years after the United States Congress added extra provisions, the Department of Agriculture had still only produced two out of three expected reports detailing precisely how the law should be carried out. The intention of the legislation was to ensure that researchers looked after the mental and physical well-being of the animals in their care. Meanwhile, a recent survey of official reports from the US Department of Agriculture showed that animals are being abused or neglected in more than four out of every five research institutions in America.

Lie number 4: *Many supporters of vivisection claim that animal experiments are required by law for all drugs, cosmetics and other chemicals. Some spokesmen say that they do not like doing animal experiments but that they have no alternative if they are going to satisfy the law.*

This is not true. Where laws do exist to control the marketing and sale of products they usually insist that products which are sold to the public must 'not be liable to cause damage to human health under normal conditions of use'.

The success of companies which *never* test their products or their ingredients on animals shows that it is perfectly possible to prepare and sell safe cosmetics (for example) which do not contain ingredients which have been tested on animals.

In my view companies which sell products which have been tested on animals or which sell products which contain ingredients which have been tested on animals do so of their own volition – often because they consider animal testing to be cheaper or more convenient than other alternatives.

The law controlling animal experiments needs to be changed and brought up to date, but I have no sympathy for companies which still try to hide behind existing legislation.

Lie number 5: *They say that all scientists approve of and support animal experiments, that animal experiments have produced an almost endless variety of valuable information and, finally, that dozens of Nobel prize winning scientists performed animal experiments as part of their award winning work.*

The first claim, that all scientists approve of and support animal experiments, is easily disproved. The Ligue Internationale Médecins pour l'Abolition de la Vivisection has nearly six hundred members – all eminent medical scientists – in twenty-eight different countries who are all opposed to animal experiments and who all believe that animal experiments are of no value whatsoever.

The second claim, that animal experiments have produced an almost endless variety of valuable information, is based on a premise that stands up less securely than a two-legged chair.

It is undeniably true that many animal experiments have been done and it is undeniably true that scientists have, over the years, discovered many valuable pieces of information. But although there may be a superficial link between these two undeniable truths, there is no deep, fundamental connection.

Indeed, a close study of scientific and medical developments during the last century or two shows quite clearly that animal experiments have hindered progress and caused far more problems than they have solved. To claim that because scientists have performed animal experiments and scientists have made valuable breakthroughs there must be a link between the two is as silly as claiming that because scientists have drunk coffee or tea the consumption of caffeine-rich drinks must be an integral part of scientific progress.

(I have dissected this argument in more precise detail on pages 53 to 75.)

Finally, there is the claim that because dozens of scientists who have performed animal experiments have won Nobel prizes there must be value in animal experiments. Once again this is an illogical claim which is based on an entirely false premise. The truth is that for decades the scientific community has accepted animal experiments as essential and has therefore excluded scientists who have not used animals in their research work from any chance of winning such honours. The vast majority of scientists winning Nobel prizes have been white males, but that merely reflects the fact that the majority of scientists being

24

eligible for Nobel prizes were white males – and that the system was heavily weighted in favour of white males winning these honours.

Lie number 6: *They say that animals do not suffer because they cannot feel pain and do not enjoy or endure any emotional responses.*

Researchers with the remnants of feelings and a vague idea of what compassion is probably like to think that all this is true.

It is not.

The prerequisites for pain reception are a central nervous system, a system of peripheral pain receptors and a series of neural connections between the receptors and the central nervous system. All vertebrate animals possess these three essentials and can undoubtedly feel pain. Anyone with a sadistic nature who doubts the truth of this should try hitting a dog or cat and watching what happens.

The argument that animals cannot feel pain is so patently absurd that it is difficult to understand why anyone should believe it to be true. The fact is, of course, that the individuals who support this argument are not overly well endowed with intelligence. I have yet to meet any researcher or supporter of vivisection whom I can credit with anything more than a most modest intellect, and I find it difficult to underestimate the intelligence of these people.

Similarly, there can be little doubt that the animals used in laboratory experiments do indeed suffer a great deal of emotional and psychological distress. During recent years a good deal of research has been done which shows just how complex and sophisticated the social behaviour of animals such as monkeys, cats and dogs can be. Observers who have studied animals know that fear and anxiety are driving forces which affect members of every species and which are, indeed, usually present as a means of self-defence. Similarly, all the animals used by experimenters suffer agonies of boredom and frustration when kept alone in small cages for long periods of time.

Lie number 7: *They accuse those who oppose vivisection of caring more for animals than for humans.*

It is difficult to imagine a more absurd or more unsustainable lie but this is, nevertheless, one which is often repeated by vivisectors who are anxious to discredit their opponents. I have lost count of the number of times I have heard it put forward – usually by mean-spirited people whose compassion and thoughtfulness for other members of the human race matches their level of compassion for the subjects of vivisection.

The truth is that I have never met a committed member of the anti-vivisection movement who was not also committed to campaigning for human rights. Just about every leading member of the anti-vivisection movement has also made loud public protests about injustice, prejudice and cruelty to human beings.

I have repeatedly been accused of caring only about animals and yet I have spent most of my life campaigning for more justice and better rights and conditions for human patients. I believe that the lives and welfare of all creatures (including humans) are closely and inextricably linked. It is absolute nonsense to claim that those who care for animals do not care for humans.

To give just one practical example, I have spent eighteen years – nearly the whole of my professional life – campaigning against the overprescribing of tranquillizers and sleeping tablets. When the authorities in Britain finally took action the then Under Secretary of State for Health and Social Security admitted that it had been my campaigning articles which had finally persuaded the government to take action.

Lie number 8: *They accuse those of us who oppose animal experiments of using emotional arguments to try to sway the uncommitted.*

This really is the pot calling the kettle black. I cannot remember when I last heard a serious opponent of vivisection using an emotional argument to sustain his or her case. The truth is that we do not need to use emotional arguments and we do not want to use emotional arguments. Those of us who oppose animal experiments know that we can do so most effectively on scientific grounds.

The trouble is, however, that our opponents – those who want animal experiments to continue – do not want to argue on scientific grounds. It is *they* who insist on using emotional arguments.

Whenever programmes about vivisection appear on television or radio stations those who support vivisection usually bring with them patients who are suffering from some disease or other. Naturally enough the patients are grateful for the treatment they have received and although they often look confused they grudgingly concede that animal experiments have to be accepted if human lives are to be saved. This is moral blackmail but it does not stop the vivisectors sitting back, looking smug and wearing 'there you are, what have you got to say to *that?*' looks on their faces.

When the supporters of vivisection speak to journalists or write newspaper or magazine articles of their own they invariably introduce the thought of patients suffering from leukaemia, diabetes or some other threatening disease. Sometimes they will even provide photographs of individual patients – preferably young and good looking.

'It is this child or a laboratory rat', they say with outrageous dishonesty. They rely on a crude form of emotional blackmail

27

that has all the subtlety of paintbrush graffiti to put the uninformed and the uncommitted into a terrible position.

The implication is always that patients' lives have been saved through animal experiments. The pro-vivisection supporters use fear and anxiety to help prosecute their argument. They know that they cannot possibly win a scientific argument and so they rely on false emotional arguments.

Lie number 9: *They say that institutions where animals are kept and experimented upon are regularly examined by skilled, impartial inspectors who make sure that animals are well looked after and treated with proper care and consideration.*

But in Britain – allegedly one of the best regulated of all countries – there are around 20,000 experimenters who have licences for animal experiments and around twenty inspectors.

This means that if every inspector visits a new scientist every day of the year (never has a day off, never takes any holidays, never falls sick, never spends time doing paperwork or attending meetings, and works weekends) then each scientist will be visited about once every three years.

However good the inspectors are, this just is not often enough to ensure that animals are well looked after and rules are obeyed. Recent figures from the Home Office in Britain show that while, in one twelve month period, the number of infringements of the rules went up by 111 per cent, the number of visits paid by inspectors to laboratories went down by 8 per cent.

Lie number 10: *They say that the Nazis disapproved of animal experiments. The clear implication is that anyone*

who disapproves of animal experiments must be in some
way comparable to the Nazis.

This is a mean-spirited, nasty little lie that commonly appears in pro-vivisection propaganda. I have frequently been called a Nazi because I oppose animal experiments. The truth is that Nazi doctors like Josef Mengele did most of their experiments on human beings because they believed that they would get better results that way. They did perform some experiments on animals, but because they had access to an unlimited supply of human experimental material they did not bother using cats, monkeys or rats very much. Mengele, for example, is said to have used 400,000 human prisoners in his experiments. Why on earth would he have wanted to bother using mice?

Lie number 11: *They say that they have to be secretive about what they do because they are frightened of being bombed by terrorist groups.*

Animal experimenters were secretive about their work long before the first bomb exploded. For decades many animal experiments have been conducted behind locked doors for the simple reason that the experimenters themselves know that what they do is so foul, so barbaric and so repugnant that if members of the public knew what they were doing there would be an outcry – and their work would be stopped.

The bombing of laboratories has been a tremendous help to animal experimenters, who have used such attacks to excuse their secrecy and to try to attract some public sympathy. Indeed, bombing campaigns have proved so successful in helping experimenters attract support that some scientists (and their supporters) have been accused of sending themselves fake bombs and fake threats.

29

Lie number 12: *When all else fails pro-vivisectionists will often claim that the results obtained in laboratory experiments can be used to help animals.*

Theoretically, it is true that drugs developed through work on rats could be used to treat rats. But does anyone seriously believe that experiments are performed on laboratory animals with the aim of finding drugs that will help those animals? And just how much effort goes into translating laboratory results into practical remedies for animals? Very little, I suspect.

The real flaw in this argument lies in the fact that even if the pro-vivisectionists were genuinely concerned about finding drugs with which to treat animal diseases they would not have to torture or kill them in order to find those drugs. The vast majority of doctors manage to find out useful things about human patients without performing evil experiments on them. The simple truth is that you do not have to kill an animal in order to find out how to help it.

3 | THE MORAL AND ETHICAL ARGUMENTS

LIKE MOST MODERN ANTI-VIVISECTIONISTS I prefer to argue against vivisection on scientific and medical grounds. But the moral and ethical arguments are important and should not be forgotten.

Moral dilemma number 1: Are animals merely 'things' which exist to be used by humankind?

René Descartes was one of the greatest thinkers in history and certainly one of the greatest men of the seventeenth century, but he had a few weaknesses and blind spots. The biggest was probably his belief that because they had no immortal soul animals had no conscious life, no desires, no feelings and no emotions.

Animals, declared Descartes with the enviable certainty of a man who is inspired by powerful religious prejudices, were no

31

more entitled to respect or consideration than were clocks; horses were no more 'alive' in the human sense than were the carriages they drew.

If Descartes had spent just a little more time looking around him and a little less time trying to understand the secrets of the universe, he would have known that he was wrong. If he had had enough common sense to talk to any child with a pet dog, cat or rabbit he would have learned the truth: that although it is impossible for us to imagine precisely how animals do think, or what they think about, there cannot possibly be any doubt that they are capable of as much thought as many humans. Simple observations would have told Descartes that animals feel pain, suffer when they are sick, get bored, endure unhappiness and depression, grieve, mourn and can be driven mad by abuse.

Each member of the animal kingdom is different, but that does not mean that cats are any less alive than Frenchmen or that dogs are any less deserving of our compassion than children. Even rats – perhaps the most despised and least lovable of laboratory animals – are intelligent, alert and sociable animals. They can develop relationships with one another and with human beings and they quickly become bored and frustrated when imprisoned.

But Descartes did not look around him and did not talk enough to children and his theories rapidly became accepted as fact by a society which was always better at thinking up theories than it was at sustaining them with facts. He was a powerful and influential member of the academic establishment and, most important of all, his beliefs fitted in comfortably with the beliefs of other scholars.

As the years went by so Cartesian logic spread throughout the scientific community and before long a scientist who wanted to look inside a cat would do so simply by nailing it to a board and cutting it open. He would ignore its squeals of protest as of little more significance than the squeaking of a rusty door hinge or a stiff axle.

To a large extent, therefore, it was Descartes' crude, simplistic and undeniably inaccurate philosophy which led to the development of modern day vivisection.

In order to keep thinking of animals as 'things' rather than sensitive individuals, most researchers have developed the habit of talking and writing about the creatures they use in a totally impersonal way, often using a strange vocabulary to describe what they are doing. Researchers will, for example, refer to cats as 'preparations', will describe crying or miaowing as 'vocalization' and will use phrases like 'nutritional insufficiency' instead of saying that animals starved to death. One group of researchers has used the term 'binocularly deprived' to describe domestic tabby kittens which they had deliberately blinded. When animals are finished with at the end of experiments they are frequently 'sacrificed' or 'subjected to euthanasia'. Maybe researchers do not like to remind themselves that they are killers.

Moral dilemma number 2: Do animals have rights?

Researchers with a simple way of looking at the world will frequently argue that animals do not have any rights. When pushed they will explain that the sole purpose of animals is to make our lives easier. The furthest they will go towards accepting that animals deserve to be treated with respect is to say that human beings share a responsibility to ensure that animals are not subjected to unnecessary suffering. The word 'unnecessary' is, of course, impossible to define satisfactorily and very few active researchers will ever admit that any experiments have ever involved 'unnecessary' suffering.

This is, of course, the same elitist talk that graced the dinner tables of the pre-Wilberforce slave traders and it is the same sort of talk that still graces the (invariably) well stocked dinner tables of the exceptionally fortunate and heavily prejudiced.

33

People, they will claim, are the centre of the universe; all else revolves around us. We, they argue, are entitled to do as we wish with the rest of the world. They will insist that if it were not for human beings animals would have no role to play on this earth. Animals, they say, exist solely to provide us with food, clothing and pleasure.

This arrogant attitude has been described as speciesism and condemned as cruel and insensitive, but these thoughts are widely held and cannot be overpowered by logic or any of the other tools of the intellectual. The primitive mind which sees humankind as the sole purpose of creation and the single reason for life is unlikely to be swayed by anything which demands such subtle expressions of intelligence as reason, insight or humility.

Moral dilemma number 3: *It is not illegal, so how can it be wrong?*

I am constantly saddened by the fact that there are still men and women around the world who regard themselves as reasonably well educated and of adequate intelligence but who can accept such a narrow, selfish and unforgiving argument. I confess that when I hear this argument aired I feel overcome by weariness and despair.

'It is against the law to torture and maim human beings in the name of science but it is not against the law to do these things to animals, so where can be the objection?'

Who can possibly live with such an absurdly mechanistic approach to life?

The truth is that what is legal is not necessarily moral, any more than what is moral is necessarily legal. A few generations ago the legal status of a black person in America was roughly similar to that of a field of corn. The truth is that what is legally acceptable and what is morally acceptable are two very different things. Most of us would agree that it is immoral to threaten or frighten children unnecessarily but such acts, when committed within a family unit, are rarely illegal. In some conditions rape may be legally acceptable. But does that make it morally right? Parking a car in the wrong place is illegal but does that make it immoral?

If we take 'legal rights equal moral rights' to its logical conclusion, consider what would happen if extra-terrestrials were to land on earth.

Under our present law no one from outer space, however charming, gentle or peace loving, could be protected from brutality. We are the only species protected by the full force of the law. A research scientist would be perfectly entitled to perform experiments on an alien, secure in the knowledge that such actions were legally proper.

It is not difficult to find many other flaws in this often voiced but shallow and remarkably simple-minded argument.

For example, are animals outside our law because they do not have souls? And if so how do we know that they do not have souls? And if it is true that they do not have souls (and are therefore denied another life) why does that give us rights over the one life that they do have?

And what about those individuals who believe in the theory of reincarnation? According to their beliefs, a scientist who chops up a mouse may be destroying a relative of theirs. Are such beliefs wrong? Do they have no legal or moral standing? Are we entitled to make judgements about our neighbours' theological beliefs simply because a written law does not forbid a particular activity?

There are no easy answers to any of these questions and I pose them simply to make it clear that there can be no inevitable agreement between activities which are legally acceptable and those which are morally acceptable.

But there is one final argument which, I think, makes it crystal clear that on balance it is dangerous to assume, as so many vivisectors do, that because their work is legal it must be moral and ethical. This final argument concerns the question of consent.

A researcher who wishes to experiment upon a human being must first obtain that individual's consent. Without consent any act of vivisection on a human being would be an illegal assault. But how can a researcher obtain consent from a monkey when planning an experiment?

Although obtaining consent is impossible we do know that monkeys can understand one another and can communicate with some human beings. So what gives a researcher the moral right either to assume that the monkey has given consent or to assume that obtaining that monkey's consent is unnecessary?

The law may say that a monkey is not a human being and therefore has no legal rights, but morally there can be no hard and fast rules about what is right and what is wrong.

Just because vivisection is legal that does *not* make it morally right.

Moral dilemma number 4: Animals do not matter because they cannot think, feel or suffer.

I have already explained that animals *can* feel pain and *can* suffer, so the only part of this argument that needs shooting down is that animals cannot think.

I first heard this argument on a television programme some years ago. The dark-suited scientist who put it forward made the statement as though it were an accepted fact and as though it excused any sort of barbarity. 'Animals can't think', he said bluntly, looking around him as though that settled that.

'What about babies?' asked a young man whose hair was dyed bright green and who had a cluster of safety pins through his nose and ears. 'Can they think?' He paused and thought for a moment. 'And what about the mentally ill, the educationally subnormal and people suffering from senile dementia?'

He was absolutely right and the scientist had no answer. The fact that animals cannot think (even if it were true) is no excuse at all for treating them without respect.

But is it true that animals cannot think? Is there any good reason to believe that a baby monkey does not *feel* when separated from its mother and family, placed in a drum and left there, alone, for several weeks at a time?

Just because animals do not automatically speak our language, do we have any right to assume that they are stupid? This is, indeed, the sort of argument once followed by the worst sort of colonial Englishman. 'The natives don't speak English and so they must be stupid', he would argue with enviable simplicity.

The truth is not so simple to find.

For example, as anyone who has ever lived with a cat will confirm it, it is nonsense to say that cats are incapable of thought. They are remarkably intelligent and emotional creatures. They can communicate with one another and with human beings very effectively. And they even have skills that we certainly do not seem to have. There are, for example, numerous accounts of cats finding their way home on journeys of several hundred miles. Cats whose owners have died will walk for miles – crossing motorways, rivers and railways and passing through cities and across fields – in order to be with other human beings whom they like. Without maps or compasses cats can make long, arduous journeys with startling skill.

We do not know how intelligent other animals are, but we do not know how stupid they are either. The only thing we know for certain is that there are no creatures in the world quite as cruel as some of the humans who work in experimental laboratories.

Those who support the use of animals in experiments also sometimes claim that those of us who oppose animal experiments are guilty of anthropomorphism and that we are worrying unnecessarily about creatures whose lives and lifestyles we do not fully understand. We are, they say, projecting our feelings, fears and hopes onto the animals they use.

There is, as ever, a strong streak of arrogance in this argument, for those who put it forward seem to be saying that although we are over-estimating the needs and rights of animals, they have got things just right.

The truth, as always, is that the pro-vivisectionist campaigners are limited by their own lack of perception and although they have managed to begin a train of thought they have been unable to see it through to a sensible conclusion. It is perfectly true to say that animals are not like people and it would be foolish to imagine that animals see things in the same way that we do. Each animal sees the world in a different light. Animals are not like people, but they are not like rocks either. Cats think and behave like cats. Monkeys think and behave like monkeys. Dogs think and behave like dogs. Only when we have made the effort to understand how dogs think and behave will we understand the full extent of their suffering when they are used in laboratory experiments.

All animals are different. Cats like eating freshly killed mice. Cows like eating grass. Monkeys use their tails to help them swing through the trees. Rats are happy eating stuff that we would feel uncomfortable about stepping in.

Although it is clearly wrong to anthropomorphize and to read ambitions and hopes into behavioural patterns that may mean something quite different, it is perfectly possible for us to learn enough about animal behaviour to understand something about what they like and what they dislike. Back in 1965 the British government decided that the thin, hexagonal wire mesh used to make up the floors of cages in which hens were kept was uncomfortable for them to walk on. A well-meaning committee of human experts decided that thicker wire would be better. But when the chickens were given the choice they showed, quite clearly, that they preferred the thin, hexagonal wire. And the chickens overruled the distinguished team who had advised the government because in the end they managed to show that they knew best what they preferred (out of two cruel options).

By observing animals carefully it is possible to decide what sort of life they like best and it is also possible to discover that when given a choice animals will always choose the least distressing of all the available options.

But the people who conduct animal experiments do not bother to find out what the animals they use are really like. They do not want to know that the animals they are using have the intelligence to make choices. They do not like to think that the animals they are keeping might prefer a different lifestyle. The truth is that the conditions in which laboratory animals are kept are crude, cruel and barbaric. The way in which animals are used and abused shows that those who perform animal experiments have never made the slightest effort to understand the creatures whose lives they regard so lightly.

The final irony is that researchers frequently claim that they can make judgements about behavioural patterns or the toxicity of tested substances by making laboratory observations. In fact, these observations and judgements are worthless because the circumstances in which the animals are kept and tested are unnatural and quite divorced from reality.

Moral dilemma number 5: *It does not matter whether animals can think or not: we are stronger and more powerful than they are so we have the right to do as we like with them.*

Surprisingly, this argument is put forward quite frequently and there seem to be a large number of vivisectors who believe that the strong have a moral right to do what they like with the weak.

What those who favour this argument do not seem to realize is that the same argument can be applied with equal logic within the human race.

So, if it is perfectly right and fair for humans to torture, maim and kill baboons because we are stronger and more powerful than they are, then it must be equally acceptable for the strongest and most powerful human beings to use the weakest humans for their own purposes.

If it is morally acceptable for a researcher to use this argument to support experiments on dogs, what is there to stop the same argument being used to justify experiments on children, old people or the mentally or physically disadvantaged?

Scientists who promote this argument might like to think carefully about their own status in our society. If the intellectually deprived and socially worthless are to be used in experiments, then the vivisectors themselves will be among the first to find themselves selected for death in the laboratory.

The truth is that if the search for knowledge is accepted as a reason for cruelty we have to be aware that it is usually difficult for scientists to draw a moral line between using animals in experiments and using human beings.

Finally, it is worth remembering that although many scientists are prepared to excuse the foulest of deeds on the basis that they are searching for knowledge, very few, if any, scientists are prepared to conduct their experiments at their own expense or in their own time. The vast majority of scientific experiments these days are performed by extremely well paid scientists working in well equipped laboratories. Often the money they use is yours.

Those members of the public who find animal experiments unacceptable (however much 'knowledge' they may give us) should also be aware that the vast majority of these experiments are conducted with public money at a time when doctors and teachers seem to agree that public services are suffering from a lack of funding.

40

I wonder how many animal experiments would carry on with their work (determined to add to the sum of human knowledge for the general good of humankind) if instead of getting fat salaries from public funds they had to pay for their experiments themselves? I suggest that some scientists would suddenly find that they had something more important to do. In other words, many vivisectors are driven not by a search for knowledge, but by simple, old-fashioned, financial greed.

Moral dilemma number 6: Animal experiments are justified because without them human progress will be held back.

One of the favourite debating tricks of those who support animal experimentation is to select a convenient date sometime in the past, point to all the scientific developments that have taken place since that time and then argue that without animal experiments none of those things would have happened.

This argument is to logic what marshmallows are to a balanced diet.

First, it is illogical to argue that just because animal experiments took place they were relevant, necessary or productive. The truth, as I will show later on, is that animal experiments have held back progress rather than aided it. You might as well argue that because people have managed to run faster and jump higher since animal experiments were started, there is a link between the two. You could as easily and as sensibly claim that the development of television was a result of experiments performed on animals and that without torturing monkeys, cats and dogs we would still be relying on the town crier.

Second, even if animal experiments had been relevant it would be absurd to argue that without them scientists would have made no progress at all. This is a gross insult to the

41

intelligence and ingenuity of scientists and assumes that the only scientists with any capacity for original though are the ones who chop up live animals. This is clearly nonsense. No one complains that we have been denied progress because scientists have not been allowed to experiment on human beings.

Moral dilemma number 7: *The use of animals in experiments is justified by the fact that such investigations enable us to add to our store of knowledge.*

Scientists usually try to justify the work they do by claiming that they are helping to save lives. They are ruthless in the way they exploit public fears and anxieties in their attempts to preserve their own careers. But such claims only stand up in the absence of evidence; more and more often scientists are having to abandon this line of defence.

When they are cornered and are unable to defend their work on practical or medical grounds, scientists will often claim that their work is justified simply because it adds to the sum of human knowledge. The work justifies itself, they say, and does not need to any have practical purpose.

It is probably as pointless to try to counter this claim with moral or ethical arguments as it would have been to try to dissuade Josef Mengele from his evil work by telling him that it was 'wrong'. Throughout history there have always been scientists who have claimed that the search for knowledge justifies any activity, however repugnant. Like the Nazi and Japanese scientists who experimented on human beings and were convinced that their work was justified, today's animal experimenters seem to believe that their work, however barbaric, is justified because it adds to the storehouse of human knowledge.

But those who are convinced by this argument might like to ask themselves where, if ever, the line should be drawn. Does the pursuit of knowledge justify *any* activity? There are some scientists who would say that it does; and there is no shortage of evidence that even today in the western world there are doctors who are willing to perform hazardous experiments on human patients under their care who have not even been asked for their permission. In my book *The Health Scandal* I described a variety of experiments, including one in which drops were put into the eyes of women in order to study the formation of experimental cataracts and one in which children were given drugs to stop them making a natural recovery from a liver infection.

Most startling of all, perhaps, were the experiments conducted by Dr Myrtle B. McGraw of Columbia University in America. McGraw used a total of forty-two babies aged between eleven days and two and a half years in her experiments, which involved holding the babies under water to see how they responded.

In the article she wrote to describe her work Dr McGraw reported that the 'movements of the extremities are of the struggling order' and went on to say that the babies clutched at the experimenter's hands and tried to wipe the water away from their faces. She seemed amazed that the 'ingestion of fluid was considerable' and made the infants cough.

During the last few decades thousands of human patients have been subjected to experimental brain surgery (readers wanting to know more should read my book *Paper Doctors*). In Britain, for example, surgeons have deliberately and permanently damaged the brains of many patients in attempts to treat people suffering from disorders as varied as eczema, asthma, hysteria, chronic rheumatism, anorexia nervosa, tuberculosis, hypertension, angina and anxiety brought about by barbiturate toxicity. Patients have been injected with cancer cells to see whether or not they developed cancer. Without anyone bothering to obtain their permission, patients around the world are frequently given new and untried drugs so that doctors can find out what happens.

43

Many scientists who perform and support animal experiments also support experiments on human beings and will argue that such experiments are justified either because they add to the sum of human knowledge or because they help doctors develop new types of treatment. One American scientist recently pointed out that 'a human life is nothing compared with a new fact . . . the aim of science is the advancement of human knowledge at any sacrifice to human life'. When another scientist was attacked for using people in a nursing home for an experiment, he replied that he could not very well use scientists for his experiments because they were too valuable.

Moral dilemma number 8: *Every year thousands of animals are 'put down' because they are ill or have been abandoned. It makes sense to use those animals instead of wasting them.*

What the scientists who favour this argument fail to realize is that there is a considerable difference between putting an animal to sleep painlessly and subjecting it to a series of painful, humiliating and degrading scientific procedures.

If this argument were sustainable then it would also make sense to use dying, lonely or 'unwanted' human beings for experiments.

The scientists who favour this argument also fail to realize that killing animals because they are ill or have been abandoned is done to satisfy human rather than animal needs. The killing of animals simply because they seem surplus to requirements is morally unjustifiable. It is absurd to attempt to build an ethical argument on foundations that are ethically unsound.

44

The final flaw

The majority of scientists who support animal experiments claim firstly that the results from animal experiments can be utilized in the prevention of treatment or diseases which affect human beings, and secondly that animals are so different from human beings that we do not have to worry about them suffering any sort of pain or distress.

These two arguments do not fit comfortably together.

If animals are similar enough to human beings for the results to be of value to clinicians then the thousands of barbaric experiments which are conducted every day are insupportable, inexcusable and unforgivable on moral and ethical grounds.

On the other hand, if animals are so fundamentally different to human beings that they do not suffer during procedures which would clearly be terrifying and enormously painful for human beings then the results obtained must be valueless.

4 | THE MEDICAL AND SCIENTIFIC ARGUMENTS

VIVISECTORS DO NOT LIKE BEING FACED with these arguments because they cannot answer them. The simple truth is that vivisection is based on a series of myths, miscalculations and misconceptions.

Scientific argument number 1: *There are differences between human beings and the animals used in experiments.*

You do not need to be a genius to realize that there are some fairly dramatic differences between a human being and a rat.

But apart from the obvious anatomical differences, there are many subtle, physiological differences between the sort of animals which are widely used in experimental procedures and the human body. In addition many of the diseases which kill or cripple human beings do not affect any other members of the

47

animal kingdom. So, for example, the cancers which affect human patients are quite different from the cancers which affect mice. Arthritis, multiple sclerosis and high blood pressure all commonly affect human beings but do not occur anywhere else in the animal kingdom. The type of tuberculosis that affects people is very different from the type that is produced artificially in animals.

There are massive differences too in the ways that drugs affect other members of the animal kingdom. Penicillin kills cats and guinea pigs but can save human beings from death by infection. Aspirin can kill cats, too, whereas it is a relatively safe and effective painkiller when taken by human patients. Arsenic is dangerous to humans but does not have anything like the same effect when given to rats, mice or sheep. Steroids damage mice in a way that they do not affect people, but thalidomide causes most problems when given to pregnant humans. Morphine sedates human beings but excites cats, goats and horses, while insulin produces deformities in chickens, rabbits and mice.

The differences are endless and doctors who have studied the subject now believe that by testing new products and procedures on animals research scientists are endangering human lives. Numerous individual drugs have been launched with great enthusiasm after animal tests have produced what seemed like optimistic results. Then, after large numbers of patients have taken the drugs, it has become clear that the original tests were misleading. It is impossible to say precisely how many patients have died or been seriously harmed because animal experiments are given far too much credence by drug companies and by agencies which are responsible for testing new drugs, but the total worldwide figure must by now run into hundreds of thousands.

A recent paper published in the *British Medical Journal* showed that four out of every ten patients who take a prescribed drug can expect to suffer severe or noticeable side effects, while numerous clinical observers agree that the incidence of iatrogenesis (medically induced disease) is now so great that approximately one in every ten hospital beds is occupied by a patient who has been made ill by their doctor. If a patient has two diseases these days it is a pretty fair bet that the second disease will have been caused by the treatment for the first. My book *The Health Scandal* contains detailed evidence showing the size of the iatrogenesis problem.

Traditionally the opposition to animal experiments has come from people who oppose vivisection on moral or ethical grounds. Much of the opposition to vivisection has come from people who like animals and are (not unreasonably) upset by the sort of unmentionable agonies which animals endure in the name of science.

The nature of the battle over vivisection is, however, changing.

For many years the majority of doctors have stood aside from the whole question of vivisection. Very few clinicians are or ever have been directly involved and relatively few have ever taken any interest in the subject.

Today, as a result of the massive epidemic of iatrogenesis which is sweeping the world and which is widely recognized as being just one of the consequences of our over-dependence upon animal experiments, a growing number of doctors are making their opposition to vivisection heard. Already the vast majority of doctors who have expressed any opinions on the subject have made it clear that they are firmly opposed to vivisection, not on ethical or moral grounds but on scientific and medical grounds. Today doctors are worried about vivisection not simply because of the damage its practitioners do to animals, but because of the damage dependence on the results they produce does to human beings.

Physicians and surgeons have repeatedly pointed out that the results obtained through animal experiments can never be applied to human patients.

'No one would test a drug intended for children on old people', argued an eminent Swiss clinician at a conference organized by the Ligue Internationale Médicins pour l'Abolition de la Vivisection and held in Berne, Switzerland. 'But we happily allow researchers to do experiments on animals which are totally different in both anatomical and physiological terms to people. It is hardly surprising that the results they obtain are worse than useless'.

An eminent American pointed out that doing toxicity tests on animals ignores the fact that many diseases are affected by what goes on in our minds. 'Animals don't suffer from stresses and anxieties in the same way as us', he argued. 'So, testing drugs on animals is bound to produce irrelevant results. Animals do suffer from stress – but their responses are different!'

'I've never given animal testing much thought before', admitted a German physician. 'But when you stop to think about it the whole system of testing drugs on animals such as rats and cats is crazy. How can you possibly hope to test a drug for high blood pressure on animals which never suffer from high blood pressure?'

Or as another doctor I spoke to put it: 'No one would test a drug for premenstrual problems on small boys and yet that would make far more sense than testing such a drug on male rats'.

Even the smallest anatomical or physiological difference can render the results of animal studies quite useless; worse, when taken seriously, they can produce dangerously misleading information. Testing drugs on mice before giving them to children is totally nonsensical. Would you allow a surgeon who had only ever practised on mice to take out your child's inflamed appendix? Would you fly in an aeroplane serviced by a man who had only ever practised on bicycles? Would it be rational to test a college examination paper out on rabbits?

The truth is that whatever its practitioners may claim, vivisection has nothing to do with science or medicine. However many animal tests are done, the first two or three generations of people who use a new drug or technique are the real guinea pigs.

Relying on animal tests means that new products which are thought to be safe are mass-marketed far too quickly and are prescribed by general practitioners and hospital doctors for thousands or even millions of patients without ever being properly assessed. It is hardly surprising that when problems occur – as they do all too frequently these days – they occur on a massive scale. Animal experiments allow drug companies to mass-market new drugs without testing them to see if they are safe and they encourage complacency among prescribing doctors who are not as alert for side affects as they should be because they have been told that the drugs they are prescribing are safe.

The consequence of our reliance on animal testing is that new and untried drugs and procedures are being tested on vast numbers of people simply so that those making those drugs or pieces of equipment can make massive profits as quickly as possible.

The real irony is that although experiments on animals are frequently used by drug companies when they want to launch new products and are desperate for information which seems to suggest that their products are safe, the same experiments are dismissed as irrelevant when they produce results which might halt or slow down the commercial exploitation of a new drug.

Indeed, the ultimate absurdity is that drug companies do deny the relevance of animal experiments when patients who have been injured by drugs or cosmetics try to use evidence obtained from animal research to help build up their cases. For example, after an American girl suffered eye damage when she had used a shampoo she tried to claim damages from the company involved on the basis that the drug also proved to be an irritant when tested on animals. However, the court in Ohio where the case was heard ruled in favour of the company on the grounds that there was no evidence to show that tests done on rabbits could be used to predict what would be likely to happen to humans.

Or consider the case of a woman who took a major international drug company to court on the grounds that the drug she had been given had damaged her sight and paralysed her. She tried producing evidence showing that the company had known for twenty years that in experiments the drug had damaged the eyesight of rabbits, had blinded and killed calves and grown cattle and had killed or paralysed dogs. The drug company denied negligence, apparently claiming that none of these results were relevant to human beings.

If these experiments were not relevant to human beings then why were they ever done? Does anyone seriously believe that chemical companies test shampoos on rabbits because they intend to sell their products to rabbits?

Sometimes the absurd reasons companies give for conducting animal experiments reach bizarre and surrealistic heights.

For example, during the last few decades cigarette companies have boasted about the millions of dollars they have spent on research. And yet whenever the results have not been considered suitable or whenever they have found themselves close to admitting that there is a link between smoking cigarettes and developing cancer, spokesmen for the cigarette companies have come up with some remarkably ingenious explanations.

Here, for example, is an exchange that took place between a lawyer representing the family of a woman who had died of lung cancer after smoking cigarettes for forty-three years and Mr Kinsey Dey, the president of a tobacco company. According to a report that first appeared in the *Wall Street Journal* and later in *The Economist*, the lawyer asked Mr Dey to explain the purpose of an experiment in which the shaven backs of mice were painted with tars derived from cigarette smoke.

MR DEY: 'To try to reduce tumours on the backs of mice.'

LAWYER: 'It had nothing to do with the health and welfare of human beings?'

MR DEY: 'That's correct'.

LAWYER: 'How much did the study cost?'

MR DEY: 'Probably more than $15 million.'

Some people of a cynical nature may find it difficult to believe that a cigarette company spent $15 million to try to save or improve the lives of mice.

Scientific argument number 2: *Although the vast majority of animal researchers are not medically qualified and have no practical, clinical experience of any kind, most of those who defend animal experiments do so on the basis that the results that are obtained by work with animals can be used to help save human lives.*

This is, in many ways, the biggest and most effective lie of all since it is the basis of the powerful emotional argument which can be summed up as the 'laboratory rat or your child' choice.

A decade or two ago animal rights campaigners and anti-vivisectionists were accused of using emotional arguments to support their case. Today, now that the anti-vivisectionists want to argue on scientific grounds, the pro-vivisection lobby is itself having to rely on an almost exclusively emotional argument.

To support that emotional argument the pro-vivisectionists will usually argue that all medical progress is due to animal experiments. But when pushed to define specific discoveries or developments which can be credited to animal experiments, they usually choose one or more from the following list. An analysis of the facts quickly shows the spurious nature of the claims that are made.

1. They claim that animal experiments have helped doctors understand heart disease and discover new treatments for

53

problems such as high blood pressure.

It is perfectly true that we know a good deal more about heart disease and high blood pressure today than we did half a century ago. It is perfectly true that doctors have access to an enormous range of pills and treatments for circulatory problems. And it is also true that thousands of animal experiments have been performed by scientists who have claimed to have been looking for cures for high blood pressure and heart disease.

But the useful information we have about the causes of high blood pressure and heart disease – stress, lack of exercise, obesity, personality type, smoking, fatty food and so on – have all been obtained by studying human beings, not cats or rats.

The enormous number of animal experiments which have been done have all been irrelevant and entirely useless. The animals used in laboratory experiments do not normally suffer from diseases such as high blood pressure. Researchers can only give the animals they use high blood pressure by tying off blood vessels, by removing kidneys or by interfering with the animal's normal physiology and anatomy so much that any resemblance to normality is purely superficial.

It is fifteen years since I first pointed out that most cases of high blood pressure could be partly if not completely controlled by teaching patients the secrets of stress control, weight loss, sensible exercise patterns and so on. Fifteen years ago this claim was regarded as heretical by the medical establishment and at least one Professor of Medicine announced that I should be silenced for daring to criticize the ubiquitous usefulness of drug therapy, but these days I doubt if there is a doctor anywhere in the world who does not now agree that I was right.

The research work that has given us the evidence we need to help understand high blood pressure and heart disease was produced not by people in white coats working in secret laboratories, but by practising clinicians working with real patients in hospitals and clinics. The useful, practical information which will help doctors control the epidemic of heart disease in the western world came from keeping good medical records and from observing patients' habits and behavioural patterns.

The most useful heart drug is still digitalis – a drug that has been used for centuries and which was obtained from the foxglove plant long before second rate scientists started demanding large chunks of public money so that they could chop up rats. Ironically, if we had relied on animal experiments to tell us whether or not digitalis was of any value, doctors would have never dared give the drug to a human patient. Digitalis is so toxic to animals that it would never have been cleared for use by humans.

The money we have poured into animal tests has been wasted. We would have saved far more lives, and improved the state of public health enormously, if we had used that money to publicize the dangers of eating too much animal fat, the dangers of cigarette smoking, the importance of regular exercise and the significance of stress.

The plain fact is that money has continued to go into animal testing because no one makes much money out of selling information about how to stay healthy. Doctors, drug companies and animal experiments all depend upon a drug-based system to make money and the only way to get drugs passed for mass-marketing quickly is to test them on animals. Animal testing has the ultimate advantage that any inconvenient problems which show up can be dismissed as irrelevant on the grounds that animal tests are irrelevant to human beings. Drug marketing is a cynical business and the drug companies know that if they tested their new products extensively on human beings very few would ever get marketed properly and profits would crash.

You do not need to be a clinical genius to realize that testing a new drug for high blood pressure on a bunch of rats who never normally suffer from high blood pressure is hardly likely to produce reliable results – and yet that is exactly what happens. Almost unbelievably, drugs that seem safe when given to animals are prescribed for millions of human patients, even though no one has any idea of the possible long term dangers.

Even the medical establishment admits that all this is true. Many eminent doctors have admitted to me privately that they know that even when a drug is licensed for mass-prescribing they have no idea what will happen when humans take it. The first patients to take a newly launched drug are guinea pigs and during the first twelve months of any drug's existence thousands of patients will suffer serious or uncomfortable side effects. The preliminary animal tests are done to enable drug companies to market their products, not to ensure safety. If you try a drug on enough different animals you can usually end up getting at least one set of results which suggests that a drug is 'safe'.

All things considered, it is hardly surprising that to say that the drugs produced to help the world's heart patients have not been an unqualified success is an understatement of heroic proportions.

Take the drug practolol for example. First introduced in the early 1970s, this drug seemed safe enough and was widely promoted as a potentially important weapon in the fight against heart disease. It was recommended for use by patients with angina and other problems, and it was advertized to family doctors who prescribed it in large quantities.

The dangers of practolol first became apparent in Britain in 1971 when, according to the Register of Adverse Reactions, published by the Committee on Safety of Medicines, a number of side effects were reported. It was not until 1974, however, that the Committee issued any warnings to doctors and not until 1975 that it was announced by the British manufacturers that the drug would only be available for hospital doctors to prescribe.

By the time family doctors had been told that they could no longer prescribe the drug, several thousand patients had suffered serious eye damage, hearing trouble and abdominal troubles. None of these symptoms were discovered when the drug was given to animals other than human beings.

56

During the last ten or fifteen years many doctors have begun to question the usefulness and safety of many other heart drugs that have been 'tested' on animals and then put onto the market. Half of all the patients taking heart drugs admit that they have noticed no change or improvement in their condition, and a massive majority of relatives and friends report that heart drugs seem to make patients with heart disease worse than they were before.

2. *They claim that animal experiments have enabled surgeons to perform successful transplant operations.*

I am constantly astonished that apparently sane individuals should try to defend animal experiments by pointing to the 'success' of transplant surgery. However, since this is an area in which the pro-vivisectionists have chosen to debate the usefulness of animal experiments, it is necessary to explain the flaws in their argument.

The basic claim made is that by chopping up animals such as dogs, surgeons can learn techniques that will help them when they start doing similar operations on people. This is simplistic nonsense. Two thousand years ago a Greek surgeon called Galen based his writings and lectures on experiments he had conducted on pigs. At the time surgeons were not allowed to chop up dead human bodies and so Galen's work was all that was available. It is, however, now generally agreed among historians that Galen's work held back medical progress for several hundred years until religious restrictions were withdrawn and doctors were allowed to cut up human cadavers. Only then did doctors discover that there are massive differences between the anatomy of the pig and the anatomy of a human.

Because they do not talk to doctors enough, the pro-vivisectionists do not realize that the majority of surgeons agree that technically there is remarkably little difference between

57

performing open heart surgery and performing a heart transplant. And the pro-vivisectionist lobby certainly cannot claim that open heart surgery owes anything at all to animal experiments. In my book *The Story of Medicine* I reported that the first open heart operation had been performed by Professor Luwig Rehn of Frankfurt, who successfully repaired a right ventricular stab wound in 1896. In the scientific paper which announced the success of his operative procedure Rehn explained that he was forced to operate by the fact that his patient was bleeding to death after being stabbed between the ribs with a kitchen knife. Just two years later surgeons were proposing to operate on the mitral valve in order to restore cardiac function. These experiments were performed on real live human patients who would have died if surgery had not been attempted.

Transplant operations have certainly been done on a wide range of animals – hearts, kidneys and even heads have been transplanted by enthusiastic experimenters – but these experiments have consistently misled surgeons rather than helped them.

If you look at the results obtained after surgeons begin performing heart transplant operations you can easily see that for the first few months the mortality rate has invariably been horrendously high. Then, steadily, the mortality rate begins to fall a little as the surgeons gain more experience of human hearts. What is clear from the figures is that the first human patients are the real 'guinea pigs'. The experiments on animals are of no practical value – though they undoubtedly help surgeons to persuade patients that the essential preliminary work has been done. The real problems occur after surgery has been performed and involve organ rejection and infection – problems which animal experiments do not help doctors overcome. Over a nine year period approximately four hundred heart transplant operations were carried out on dogs but the first human patients died because of complications that had not arisen in animal experiments. Differences in anatomy and physiology mean that the results obtained from animal experiments cannot be used to help surgeons operating on human beings.

But in a way all this misses the point.

The real problem with transplant operations is that they are an absurdly expensive and impractical luxury which no country, however rich, can possibly afford. Fifteen years ago, when I wrote my book *Paper Doctors*, I quoted Professor Alfred Pletscher who had pointed out that the French could easily spend every penny allocated for health care just on providing patients with new or artificial kidneys. The same is true for every other country and for every type of organ transplant.

About one in every hundred people in developed countries suffers from heart pains, and heart disease is a major cause of death. No country could possibly offer heart transplant operations to all the patients who need them. The cost would, quite simply, be prohibitive. In Britain, for example, the cost of providing heart transplants for everyone who needed one would be approximately £10 billion in the first year. In the second year that figure would go up dramatically as many of the patients who had already received transplants needed a second transplant. Even if you ignore the question of where all the hearts are going to come from, it is not difficult to see that within a very short space of time Britain would be spending its entire gross national product on heart transplant surgery. Everything else – education, defence, roads and so on – would have to be shelved. There would be no money for looking after the young or the old, no money for treating patients with cancer, arthritis or kidney disease and no money for family doctors, ambulances or fire engines.

Recognizing this, the amount of money allocated for transplant surgery is kept to a modest figure and doctors pick out patients for transplants with the same sort of fairness with which lottery organizers decide who will win the big prize. If you are good looking and you have an interesting job and a bright personality then you may get on the list for a transplant. If you are ugly, poor or unemployed then you probably will not.

The simple, inescapable truth is that we could save a thousand times as many lives if all the money being spent on transplant surgery was instead spent on persuading people to smoke less, eat less fat, take more exercise, lose weight and learn to deal with the stress in their lives.

Animal researchers may claim that their work helps transplant surgeons. But they are not only wrong, they are also backing a technology that is obsolete before it comes of age. It is no coincidence that Britain, which has for years led the world in transplant surgery, has one of the highest death rates from heart disease in the world.

3. *They claim that animal experiments have given us powerful antibiotics – such as penicillin – which have enabled doctors to control infectious diseases that used to kill millions of people every year.*

There are two flaws in this particular argument.

The first flaw is in saying that animal experiments had any useful part to play in the discovery and development of antibiotics.

When Alexander Fleming discovered penicillin growing on a culture dish in 1928 he tested the drug on rabbits and discarded it when it seemed useless. Later the drug was tested on a cat and a human patient at the same time. The cat died and the human being lived. If doctors had relied upon animal experiments to decide whether or not penicillin was of any value the drug would have been discarded long ago.

The second flaw lies in the argument that antibiotics have enabled doctors to control infectious diseases. The truth (explained at some length in my book *The Story of Medicine*) is that the advances in public health which led to a reduction in death rates from infectious diseases during the nineteenth century were not a result of new drugs, new surgical techniques or

60

vaccines, but were instead a result of improvements in water supplies, sewage facilities, food supplies and housing conditions.

When graphs are prepared showing the death rates from infectious diseases such as pneumonia, typhoid, cholera, tuberculosis and whooping cough it quickly becomes clear that the death rates from all major infectious diseases had fallen dramatically long before useful drugs had been discovered and introduced onto the market. It was simple improvements in standards of living which did the trick – not new 'wonder' drugs.

Among those who support animal experiments are a large, feeble-minded group whose understanding of history is as slight as their understanding of science.

4. *They claim that it was as a result of animal experiments that the death rate among pregnant women and newborn babies fell dramatically during the second half of the nineteenth century.*

Once again the pro-animal-experiments lobby is way off course with their claims. It was not drugs or surgical practices that helped ensure that more babies lived and fewer pregnant women died, but better hygiene in the delivery room.

The first doctor to recognize that puerperal fever might be prevented by keeping the maternity ward as clean as possible was a surgeon called Charles White who practised in Manchester, England, in the late eighteenth century. White's observations and recommendations attracted little attention and lying-in wards remained dirty, dangerous places for several decades.

In 1843 the American poet, novelist, anatomist and lecturer Oliver Wendell Holmes read to the Boston Society for Medical Improvement a paper entitled 'On the Contagiousness of Puerperal Fever' in which he explained his theory that the disease could be carried from patient to patient by doctors themselves. Holmes recommended that in order to reduce the risk of death, women in labour should not be attended by doctors who had been in contact with possible sources of infection. He also suggested that surgeons could consider changing their clothes and washing their hands after leaving patients who did have infections. His controversial lecture annoyed many doctors and his advice was ignored.

In 1846 Philipp Semmelweiss became assistant in one of the obstetric wards at the Allgemeines Krankenhaus in Vienna. Semmelweiss, who was twenty-eight years old, noticed that the number of women dying in his ward was considerably higher than in another obstetric ward at the same hospital. Indeed, the difference was so noticeable that women frequently begged in tears not to be taken into Semmelweiss's ward.

Deciding that the difference in the number of deaths had to be due to something other than the quality of his own clinical skills, Semmelweiss looked for an explanation and found that the only difference between the two wards was that the women who had a better chance of survival were looked after by the hospital's midwives, while the women in his own ward were looked after by medical students.

Semmelweiss's next discovery was that the students came into the ward straight from the dissecting room and often performed intimate examinations with hands which had, only minutes before, been delving into decaying corpses. The midwives never went near the dissecting room.

Semmelweiss's theory that the pregnant women were catching the infection from the students was strengthened when he attended a post mortem on a Dr Kolletschka who had died from a wound he had received in the dissecting room. Semmelweiss noticed that the inside of Kolletschka's body showed the same pathological signs displayed by the women with puerperal fever.

Convinced that his theory about the spread of infection was right, Semmelweiss insisted that students and doctors coming from the dissecting room should wash their hands thoroughly before examining female patients. The precautions he introduced produced a dramatic drop in the number of deaths in his ward – from one in ten patients to one in a hundred patients within two years.

Sadly, Semmelweiss was bitterly opposed by colleagues at the hospital who disagreed with his theory, probably because they would have preferred experimental evidence obtained by work done on animals. The pressure and controversy proved too much for an essentially mild and thoughtful man, who died in a mental hospital a few years later.

Those who believe in the efficacy of animal experimentation would have us forget the work of Philipp Semmelweiss and give credit to experiments performed in laboratories. But the real truth is undeniable.

5. *Pro-vivisection lobbyists have announced that tranquillizers were developed with the help of animal experiments.*

The first time I heard this claim my mouth fell open in disbelief. It is perfectly true that animal experiments were used during the development of the benzodiazepine tranquillizers, but if the supporters of vivisection had done more research before speaking they would have learned that it was the failure of those animal experiments to show the addictive nature of the benzodiazepines which has led to tens of millions of people around the world getting hooked on prescribed drugs.

One of the many shortcomings of animal tests is that for fairly obvious reasons they do not check the psychological hazards associated with products which are under test. Even if animals do become physically or psychologically dependent on drugs they are unlikely to be able to complain about this fact and researchers are unlikely to be observant enough to realize what is happening.

The addictive nature of the benzodiazepines only became apparent when the drugs were prescribed for human patients.

63

By the time the existence of this problem had been generally recognized by the manufacturing companies, official watch-dog groups and the medical profession, the drugs had been pre-scribed for millions of patients over a twenty year period.

It took me fifteen years – from 1973 to 1988 – to persuade the authorities in Britain that benzodiazepine tranquillizers are potentially addictive and need to be treated with caution by everyone associated with their use.

I believe that the original animal experiments were, to a large extent, responsible for this reluctance to recognize that a prob-lem existed. Too many members of the medical establishment give credence to animal experiments and once such work has been done an air of complacency develops. Commercial, legal and professional pressures ensure that clinical observations – however widespread they may be – take second place to the original, long established animal experiments.

6. *Animal research supporters say that without animal experiments there would never have been a vaccine against poliomyelitis – and that the disease would have killed millions more.*

Once again the pro-vivisection lobby is wrong for two reasons.

First, they are wrong because the number of deaths from poliomyelitis had already fallen dramatically before the first poliomyelitis vaccine was introduced. As with other infectious diseases, the significance of poliomyelitis had dropped as better sanitation, better housing, cleaner water and better food had been introduced in the second half of the nineteenth century. It was social developments rather than medical ones which in-creased human resistance to infectious diseases. Proof that the introduction of the vaccine was not the success it was made out to be comes from undeniable statistics. In Tennessee, USA, the number of poliomyelitis victims the year before vaccination became compulsory was 119, but the year after vaccination was introduced the number rose to 386. In North Carolina the number of cases before vaccination was introduced was 78, while the number after the vaccine became compulsory rose to 313. There are similar figures for other American states.

Second, they are wrong because although an early breakthrough in the development of a poliomyelitis vaccine was made in 1949 with the aid of a human tissue culture, monkey kidney tissue was used when the first practical vaccine was prepared in the 1950s. The monkey tissue was used simply because that was standard laboratory practice, but no one realized that one of the viruses commonly found in monkey kidney cells can cause cancer in human beings. If human cells had been used to prepare the vaccine (as they could have been and as they are now) the original poliomyelitis vaccine would have been much safer.

Incidentally, some pro-vivisectionists do still claim that animal tests help ensure that batches of poliomyelitis vaccine are safe for human use. This is nonsense. Ten years ago a spokesman for the World Health Organization estimated that 180,000 mice, 30,000 guinea pigs and 60,000 rabbits had been used without adding anything to the safety of poliomyelitis vaccine. In 1982 the World Health Organization recommended that such tests need not be done when human cells are used to produce the vaccine.

7. A common and very emotional claim made by those who have a personal or commercial interest in seeing animal experiments continue is that such experiments are the only hope of finding a cure for AIDS. I have even seen AIDS victims taken into TV studios to argue that animal experiments are their only hope.

This is one of the sickest and cruellest of all the ploys used by the vivisectionists.

The truth is that although monkeys have been deliberately infected with the HIV virus (the one that causes AIDS), no researchers have yet been able to give human AIDS to any known laboratory animal. Even if they manage to succeed in this perverse aim their experiments will be a waste of time, effort and money.

Worse, there is simple evidence now to suggest that the development of the AIDS virus was originally a result of animal experiments performed by research scientists messing around with viruses and laboratory animals. Throughout the 1960s and 1970s researchers all over America were busy transmitting viruses from one monkey to another to see what happened. New viruses were developed with enthusiasm and passed from one species to another. Researchers even swapped viruses between laboratories to test out their personal theories. Experimenters deliberately tried to combine different viruses to see what happened.

No effective attempts were made to control or contain the viruses which were thought (rather stupidly perhaps) to affect only laboratory animals. It now seems startlingly clear that what eventually happened was that a new and virulent virus was transmitted from an animal (probably a monkey) to a laboratory worker.

Anyone who doubts that a virus developed in a laboratory can get out into the real world should remember that the last smallpox scare we know of originated when a laboratory worker in Birmingham, England, was infected with the disease. The United States Army Biological Warfare Establishment has a predictably high level of security, but in twenty-five years there have been an average of one accident every three to four weeks – with 423 cases of serious infection.

Because of misleading propaganda published by pressure groups many people still mistakenly believe that AIDS is a sexually transmitted disease. It is not. It is a blood-borne disease which can be transmitted by any activity which leads to an exchange of body fluids. Officially inspired fears and sponsored prejudices have led to so much confusion that the original source of the disease has remained shrouded in mystery. There are, however, many experts who now believe that although animal experimenters are not going to find a cure for AIDS, it was they who gave the world the disease.

8. *Arthritis is one of the commonest of the crippling and disabling diseases. It is a major source of income to many of the world's biggest drug companies. Researchers frequently claim that animal experiments have helped scientists produce many new and valuable drugs – and they warn that without animal experiments there will never be a cure for the disease.*

Once again these are callous and premeditated lies designed to help people make profits.

During the last few decades the world's drug companies have, with the aid of animal tests, produced an almost unending series of anti-inflammatory drugs which have had to be withdrawn after serious and sometimes lethal side effects have been reported. Hundreds of patients have been killed and thousands have been injured by drugs which were introduced to help combat a group of diseases which may be painful but do not kill.

One of the problems drug company researchers have faced is that laboratory animals do not suffer from arthritis. So, to test new drugs, researchers have to inject the joints of rats, rabbits and mice with irritating chemicals in an attempt to produce some inflammation of the end of the bones. It is not arthritis, but it is the best the researchers can do.

Even more senseless have been experiments performed to try and see if dietary changes have any effect on these false examples of arthritis. Trying out new foods and combinations of foods on rats or genetically identical mice who have artificial arthritis is as absurd and as unnecessary as it sounds. It is absurd because rats do not eat the same sort of foodstuffs as human beings and so are not likely to respond usefully to what is for them an unnatural diet. It is absurd because human beings are not genetically identical. And it is unnecessary because there is no shortage of real, live, human patients prepared to try different diets to see if their arthritis is improved by less of this or more of that.

The final proof of the absurdity of trying to find cures for arthritis with the aid of animal experiments lies with the drug aspirin – the best established and most widely used pain reliever and anti-inflammatory drug in the world. Aspirin – obtained from the willow tree – has been used for centuries (in 1763 the Royal Society was informed of the effectiveness of a compound prepared from willow bark) and, despite the claims of companies trying to promote their very latest and very expensive products, is widely regarded as one of the safest and most effective drugs available. But although aspirin works well on human beings suffering from arthritis it can be toxic to rats, mice, dogs, cats, monkeys and guinea pigs – whether they are suffering from fake arthritis or not. If our ancestors had insisted on testing aspirin on laboratory animals it would have been abandoned long ago as far too dangerous.

9. *Every time I go on television or appear on the radio to explain why animal experiments are useless the presenter or interviewer will point a finger at me and tell me that without experiments on animals insulin would not have been discovered and diabetes would not have been conquered.*

The presenters (or, more likely, their researchers) invariably get this misleading information from the pro-vivisection lobbyists. It is, predictably, yet another piece of nonsense.

Sometimes the supporters of animal experiments become so desperate that they construct remarkably complex and infinitely fragile scenarios to make their case appear stronger. For example, on one television programme on which I appeared a vocal supporter of animal experiments claimed that South Africa would be a different country today if it had not been for animal experiments. His evidence for this claim was that the Right Reverend Desmond Tutu had been introduced into the church by a man who had diabetes. Even if animal experiments had been necessary or relevant to keep the individual concerned alive, it is difficult to believe that Tutu's conversion was entirely dependent upon the conviction of one man. This sort of flimsy scenario would normally be rejected out of hand by tough television presenters, but when discussing animal experiments many seem unwilling to take issue with any argument, however imaginative, put forward by spokesmen and women for the medical and pharmaceutical establishments.

The truth about diabetes is very different, though far less dramatic.

First, it is absurd nonsense to claim that diabetes has been cured. For over half a century the number of people dying of diabetes has increased fairly dramatically. Today the incidence of diabetes is doubling every ten years.

Second, the discovery of insulin was relevant only to a relatively small number of patients. Today the great majority of diabetics who develop diabetes as adults control their disease through diet – they certainly do not need insulin injections.

Third, rather than helping diabetics animal experiments put back progress by many decades.

The first link between the pancreas gland and diabetes was established back in 1788 – without any animal experiments – by a doctor called Thomas Cawley who had examined the body of a patient who had died of the disease. Before this another observant physician called Matthew Dobson had, in 1766, shown that the urine of diabetics is loaded with sugar.

Sadly, these hopeful beginnings did not lead to much because for the whole of the nineteenth century researchers tried to produce diabetes in animals by damaging their pancreas glands and failed miserably to get any useful, practical or relevant results.

Faith in animal experiments was as high then as it is now and no doctor dared do anything until the laboratory scientists had produced evidence to back up the early work of Dobson and Cawley.

Finally, in the early part of the twentieth century, three scientists called Banting, Best and Macleod did manage to extract insulin from the pancreas of a dog and the much delayed clinical work on diabetes could continue. It had taken one hundred and fifty years of work and enormous numbers of animals had been killed.

If animal experiments had been banned two centuries ago the chances are high that we would by now understand a good deal more about diabetes. Today scientists believe that in many cases the disease is related to diet and other environmental factors and there is no doubt that in future progress will be made by observant clinicians, not laboratory research workers.

10. *'Cancer' is a word that frightens people and the pro-vivisectionists are not averse to using that fear to help defend themselves and what they do.*

Time and time again those who support animal experiments claim that work done on mice, rats, cats, dogs and monkeys will help produce drugs and techniques which will enable us to conquer cancer. I have lost count of the number of times that I have heard pro-vivisectionists argue that animal experiments have already helped in the production of anti-cancer therapies. And I have lost count of the number of times that I have heard people collecting public money for laboratory experiments claim that a major breakthrough is just around the corner and that researchers need just a few more million pounds to perform a few more experiments.

The real truth is very different. The real truth is that the available evidence shows that animal experiments are a waste of time, that animal experiments have never led to any useful breakthrough and that they are never likely to lead to any useful breakthroughs. The simple, unvarnished truth is that animals get different types of cancer to human beings, animals respond quite differently to drugs and the cancers animals get respond very different when treated with drugs. Indeed, the evidence shows that instead of helping doctors, researchers working with animals have held back medical progress and have been responsible for hundreds of thousands of deaths.

Just look at the facts.

First, to talk about cancer as though it was a single disease is inaccurate and misleading. It is, indeed, rather like talking about 'infection' as though there were only one type of known infection. Clinicians have identified approximately two hundred types of cancer – most of which are very different. It is absurd to spend millions looking for a general cure for cancer (as many of the researchers using animals do) because there cannot possibly be a single treatment that will 'cure' so many different diseases. By continuing to hunt for a 'magic' solution animal experimenters display their basic ignorance.

Second, trying to find out if chemicals cause cancer by testing them on animals is less efficient than tossing a coin. American toxicologist David Salsburg has shown that the standard test used on rats gives results which can be applied accurately to human beings just 38 per cent of the time. Put another way, that means that 62 per cent of the time the results animal experiments obtain are wrong. Tossing a coin would at least give a 50 per cent chance of success. Animal tests are inaccurate for the simple reason that animals used in laboratory experiments are different from people. According to Dr Irwin Bross, giving evidence to the United States Congress, 'conflicting animal results have often delayed and hampered the war on cancer, they have never produced a single, substantial advance either in the prevention or treatment of human cancer'.

Time and time again cancer specialists who have looked critically at animal experiments have concluded that such experiments are far worse than useless. Dr Doyen, a French cancer specialist, said:

> *Experiments on animals are really unsatisfactory as it is*
> *never possible to be certain that animals are liable to the same*
> *diseases as mankind and in the same form, and in many cases*
> *we know that the contrary is the case.*

Professor Hastings Gilford concluded a long study of cancer experiments by saying:

> *It has fallen to my lot to have to make a general survey of*
> *cancer in all its aspects and I do not believe that anyone who*
> *does this with an open mind can come to any other*
> *conclusion than that to search for the cause or cure of cancer*
> *by means of experiments on lower animals is useless. Time*
> *and money are spent in vain.*

And even the medical journal *The Lancet* carried the thought that 'since no animal tumour is closely related to a cancer in human beings an agent which is active in the laboratory may well prove useless clinically'.

Third, America's Food and Drug Administration has produced a 'test bed' made of human muscle tissue cells which can be used reliably to test anti-cancer drugs. What would you prefer to take: a drug tested on mice or one tested on cells exactly similar to the ones in your own body?

Fourth, we know what causes 80 per cent of all cancers. We have for years known enough about the things which cause cancer to be able to prevent the disease developing in the majority of people who develop it. If we really wanted to reduce the incidence of cancer we could do so easily by controlling chemicals more effectively, by providing more powerful warnings about smoking tobacco and by telling people that fatty foods cause cancers of the breast, womb and colon. The politicians do not do any of these things because the people who manufacture chemicals and cigarettes are rich and powerful. A true cynic might say that the medical establishment continues to support animal experiments precisely because it knows that they will not produce any useful results but will help to protect the status quo. Time and time again in my books and articles I have provided evidence to show that the medical profession and the drugs industry are closely interlinked; there can be few people who are not now aware that drug company money has bought the loyalty of many leading members of the medical profession around the world.

Fifth, all the useful evidence we have accumulated about cancer has come from human studies. The links between chemicals, X-rays, foods and asbestos on the one hand and different types of cancer on the other hand were all obtained after doctors had studied human patients. Instead of helping, animal experiments have consistently slowed down the speed with which these essential discoveries have been accepted.

For example, the link between tobacco smoke and cancer was spotted decades ago by doctors working with human patients, but animal experiments were used as an excuse by politicians who wanted to avoid taking action against (and therefore annoying) the wealthy tobacco companies. Researchers spent decades making beagles smoke cigarettes and painting tobacco tar on the backs of mice in attempts to establish a laboratory link between tobacco and cancer – a link which was not needed since links clearly existed between tobacco and human cancer. The decades of vague and inconclusive results which were obtained gave the tobacco companies a chance to keep the confusion going and to prevent doctors giving their patients authoritative warnings about smoking tobacco. Doctors *knew* that cigarettes caused cancer but were encouraged to keep quiet while animal researchers spent years failing (quite predictably) to obtain any conclusive results.

The industries which have used animal research to disguise, distort and bury the truth have had things made easy for them because most of us have not really wanted to know the truth. We have subconsciously welcomed their delaying tactics because they have given us an excuse to carry on with our bad habits without feeling too bad about them. Similarly, we have been encouraged to continue smoking our cigarettes, eating vast quantities of animal fats and putting up with polluted air because we have been convinced that the animal researchers will find easy solutions to our problems that will not involve us in doing anything that we do not like. We have been conned into thinking that the easy way to fight cancer is to make an annual donation to a cancer research charity, and allowed to think that with someone busily looking for a cure we can safely carry on with all the things that, deep down, we know are bad for us.

I have deliberately limited myself to exposing the lies inherent in ten of the most commonly publicized claims made by the pro-vivisectors, in order to keep this book to a manageable length. I could easily destroy *any* claim that *any* animal experimenter cared to put forward. For example, a supporter of vivisection insisted recently that experiments on animals had led to magnificent advances in the treatment of stomach diseases. Unfortunately, the vivisector had not done his homework properly. If he had he would have known that back in 1951 *The Lancet* warned that: 'the gastrointestinal tract in man is unfortunately very different from that in animals and the results of a new operation for gastric disease cannot be predicted from operations on dogs'.

Researchers frequently claim that the thousands of experiments conducted on monkeys, dogs and other animals at secret government establishments are designed to help human beings, but surgeons treating casualties at the Royal Victoria Hospital in Belfast, Northern Ireland, have stated firmly that 'nothing they could have learned at Porton Down (Britain's Ministry of Defence research establishment) could be of help to us here in Belfast' and have asked: 'How can they justify shooting animals – that aren't like humans anyway – just to see what the wounds are like?'

Scientific argument number 3: *Animal experiments have been a hindrance not a help to doctors.*

I have already shown how the medical establishment's obsession with animal experiments delayed the ability of doctors to do anything useful to help diabetes and helped prevent the day when doctors could help cut down the number of deaths from lung cancer by warning of the risks associated with tobacco. But these are by no means the only examples which show that animal research work has held back medical progress and has undoubtedly been responsible for countless thousands of deaths during the last century or two.

Time and time again doctors have been dangerously misled by animal experiments and patients have died because scientists have convinced doctors that their results were relevant. The practical treatment of infectious diseases such as poliomyelitis and tuberculosis was confused and delayed because doctors did not realize that the laboratory research work that had been done could not safely be transferred to clinical practice. The evidence also clearly shows that animal experiments delayed the practical availability of blood transfusions and led directly to the deaths of patients.

The first attempts to put fresh animal's blood (from a lamb) into a sick patient were made in 1667 by Jean Baptiste Denys who

75

was Professor of Philosophy at Montpellier and court physician to Louis XIV. Unfortunately, Denys found himself under arrest after at least one patient ended up in the cemetery and the practice of transfusing blood from animals into humans was prohibited in France by an Act of the Chamber of Deputies in 1668. Despite this the idea of taking blood out of animals and putting it into humans seemed to fascinate the world and in Italy a physician called Francesco Folli wrote a book on the subject. In England such eminent authors as Christopher Wren, Robert Boyle and Samuel Pepys all wrote on the subject.

The animal experiments did not get anyone anywhere however and it was not until over two centuries later, when the biologist Landsteiner decided to concentrate on human blood, that any progress was made. Landsteiner discovered that different human beings have different types of blood and his work made blood transfusion a practical possibility.

Supporters of vivisection sometimes claim that the early animal work had helped in the development of transfusion, but the history books show clearly that it did not. Indeed, those early animal experiments held back progress by over two centuries. Incidentally, some vivisectors also point to the use of the term rhesus to describe a blood grouping as evidence that animal experiments have helped in this area. Once again the factual evidence shows that they are wrong. The rhesus factor was discovered in human patients by a doctor in New York in 1939, but animal researchers who did later research work to confirm what doctors already knew used rhesus monkeys.

Animal experiments have hindered doctors by producing an almost endless series of misleading results. Some experiments have falsely suggested that some drugs will be safe. Other experiments have, with equal apparent accuracy, suggested that other drugs are unlikely to be either safe or effective. If doctors had taken proper notice of animal experiments then vital drugs such as penicillin, morphine, digitalis and aspirin would have been banned from human use.

The evidence is clear and unequivocal. Animal experiments have done no good, but have done a great deal of harm.

Scientific argument number 4: *The quality of work done by animal researchers is so low that even if their results were relevant they would not be reliable.*

Many of the procedures used when testing drugs or chemicals on animals are badly designed, unpredictable and illogical. Much of the work done by vivisectors is secret (ostensibly because the researchers are worried about the activities of animal rights extremists, but in reality because they are worried that if details of their work become public knowledge then members of the public will be so outraged that research work on animals will be stopped). However, in order to maintain their academic status and to keep the money coming in the vivisectors have to publish scientific papers describing what they have done.

When these reports are carefully assessed it becomes clear that the majority of experiments are sloppily designed, that procedures are executed without skill or any true understanding of any of the basic principles of science and that the conclusions which they draw cannot possibly be sustained. Even if the vivisectors were simply trying to find out how to prevent cancer developing in rats (rather than hoping to use their results to draw conclusions about the treatment of cancer in human beings) their results would be valueless simply because their experiments are so badly designed.

So, for example, the vast majority of experiments are conducted by researchers who seem blissfully unaware that there are vast differences between the behaviour of an animal artificially restrained within a cage and the behaviour of an animal looking after itself in the wild. Researchers make no attempt to mimic the natural diet of the animals they use in their experiments and most do not even attempt to standardize the diet given to the animals they use. Doctors know that giving drugs to patients in abnormal circumstances dramatically alters the results they get. But what could be more unnatural than giving drugs to animals in cages? All animal tests done in laboratories are done in abnormal circumstances.

Even more significant is the fact that the vast majority of vivisectors seem totally unaware of the role that stress plays in the development of disease. Every doctor now understands that stress has a tremendous influence on the development of disease and even in abattoirs workers recognize that the amount of stress an animal suffers before it is killed so affects its hormone levels that the taste and texture of the meat obtained can be affected; but vivisectors still seem to ignore this factor.

If they had read the relevant scientific literature they would soon discover that there is a good deal of evidence (in scientific papers going back as far as 1973) to show that animals which are under stress do not make reliable experimental subjects, for stress and anxiety can accelerate the growth of tumours and make animals vulnerable to a wide range of infections.

Such constraints alone are bad enough but there is worse to come, for there is also a considerable amount of evidence available to show that a remarkably large number of researchers are so desperate for results that they will deliberately fake their experiments in order to substantiate the conclusions they want to draw. The constant quest for status and money means that today's scientists are too often concerned more with obtaining the results they think they should obtain (or the results their employers want them to obtain) than with practising good science.

In one of my early books I described the case of Dr William Summerlin who was hired by the Sloan Kettering Institute in New York to do work on the problem of transplanting skin and overcoming rejection problems.

Summerlin seemed to have made a major breakthrough in this area but no other laboratory anywhere else in the world was able to duplicate his excellent results and eventually, under pressure, Summerlin admitted that he had helped his experiments along a little. He was supposed to have transplanted skin from black mice to white mice. In fact he had simply inked in the transplant sites with a black felt-tipped pen.

During the last few years there have been numerous such scandals and reputable establishments all around the world have had to admit to having sponsored misleading or dishonest medical research. Some fraudulent work has been subtle. But some has been crude – as, for example, was the work of the researcher who killed dozens of rats in order to cover up an experiment which contradicted the results of a previous experiment.

This massive turn towards fraud has badly damaged the quality of research work in establishments all around the world. Even establishments where researchers are still honest have been contaminated, because once a fraudulent paper gets into the system it can be quoted hundreds of times by other researchers within months of its first publication.

There is, amazingly, no way for researchers to check on the validity of the papers they want to use in their own research work. The size of the problem can easily be illustrated by the fact that when Robert Slutsky of the University of California withdrew fifteen published papers after a flurry of activity which had seen him producing new scientific papers at the rate of one every ten days, his action put fifty-five other scientific papers under a cloud.

Even when researchers are not overtly dishonest, their inability to use statistical procedures properly means that the conclusions that are drawn are frequently invalid. One major survey of research work showed that almost 75 per cent of all the work published contains invalid conclusions. An eminent American scientist recently testified before the United States

Congress that he believed that 25 per cent of scientific papers are now based at least in part on data that have been intentionally fudged.

The sad truth is that science, as practised by animal experimenters, has been contaminated by greed and conceit, and the quest for bigger grants, bigger laboratories, more diplomas and more published papers has taken over from the simple search for truth. Most of the men and women who perform animal experiments are neither qualified doctors nor qualified veterinary surgeons, and their understanding of the science of statistics is often limited.

The modern animal researcher is, in my view, a disgrace to the world of science and a disgrace to logic and clear thinking. It is hardly surprising that scientists continue to perform animal experiments which are purposeless and pointless.

Scientific argument number 5: *Animal experiments have an adverse effect on those who perform them and 'dehumanize' medical students and doctors.*

The people who perform animal experiments professionally are, by and large, no longer sensitive or intelligent beings. Talk to one for a few minutes and you will quickly discover that.

But this is not particularly surprising. If animal experimenters were sensitive or intelligent people, would they be able to do what they do?

The real danger is that students who are forced to undertake animal experiments as part of their studies will become so hardened by the suffering and the daily deaths they see that they become permanently desensitized to suffering.

And there is real evidence to show that this does happen. Alice Heim, a psychologist, has shown that students and teachers are desensitized by doing laboratory work with ani-

80

mals, and other authors have expressed their fears about the ways in which animal experiments encourage an inhumane approach to life among students.

Scientific argument number 6: *Some of the tests performed are grotesquely barbaric and absurdly unreliable.*

Of all the tests performed routinely in animal laboratories the two most indefensible are almost certainly the LD50 test and the Draize Eye Irritancy Test.

In theory the LD50 test is designed to find out how toxic different substances are – yet it is difficult to imagine a more pointless or unreliable laboratory experiment. The letters LD stand for 'lethal dose' and the '50' denotes the fact that this test is designed to find the dose necessary to kill 50 per cent of the animals used. The LD50 test was devised in 1927 to help measure drug strengths, but used in this obscene way it has, over the years, resulted in millions of animal deaths.

Even scientists know that the test is nothing more than an absurd ritual and that the results of the test are affected by the animal's age, general health, sex, diet and so on. Factors as delicate as the type of bedding used have been shown to influence experimental results and some scientists acknowledge that in many cases animals die not because of the toxic effects of the substances they are forced to consume but because of the bulk of the material. If you force a dog to swallow cupfuls of shampoo or toothpaste or talcum powder or soap, its health is bound to suffer because its stomach just is not large enough.

The test is so unreliable that surveys have shown that LD50 values vary by as much as fourteen times according to which factors are changed – even when the substance is tested on identical animals. However, when the LD50 test is done on different strains of rat the variations can be as much as 450 times. These massive variations mean that LD50 results really are worse than useless.

In recent years an allegedly 'humane' version of the LD50 test has been introduced into some laboratories. In this test a low dose of the substance being used is given to a very small group of animals and as soon as any severe side effects begin to develop the animals are killed. However 'humane' this new test may be, I do not believe for a second that it can possibly be any more reliable than its predecessor. Some politicians and experimental scientists claim that this new test has replaced the LD50 test, but that is not true – around the world millions of animals are still killed every year in totally pointless LD50 tests.

The harsh, stark truth is that it would make just as much sense to test the safety of motor cars by filling them with animals, crashing the cars and then counting the dead bodies. In fact such a test would be of arguably more scientific value than the LD50 test.

In the Draize Eye Irritancy Test substances such as pesticides, hairsprays and detergents are dropped into an animal's eye and left there for days or weeks to see what happens. Rabbits are usually chosen for this experiment because they are cheap to buy and have large, easily accessible eyes (the fact that they are docile creatures helps because this experiment is barbaric beyond words and no anaesthetic is used).

It does not take much of an imagination to understand what happens. Slowly, the rabbits' eyes become red and swollen; then they become ulcerated and start to bleed. The whole of the eye becomes inflamed and swells up and the pain must be unbelievably excruciating without an anaesthetic. But for the unfortunate rabbit there is no respite; the test continues so that the researchers can make careful notes about what happens as the eyes are slowly destroyed.

The Draize Eye Irritancy Test would be unjustifiable if it helped save human lives. But it does not. It is probably one of the

82

most futile and utterly pointless tests ever devised and it is nothing but a tribute to human cruelty and wickedness. The research scientists who perform this test for a living are, in my opinion, surely sub-human.

There are several quite specific problems with this test.

First, it is totally irrelevant to human beings. It would make as much sense (and be considerably less barbaric and more reliable) to test chemicals by dropping them onto sheets of paper and watching what happened. The rabbit's eye cannot be usefully compared to any human tissue or organ.

Second, the test is totally subjective. The scientist who makes the assessment scores the eye damage according to redness, swelling and discharge. But there is no way to ensure that different scientists assess damage in the same way. Even though all the scientists performing the Draize Test do have one thing in common (they are sub-human), the variations between one sub-human scientist and another are phenomenal.

Third, there is an effective, efficient alternative available, using an artificial preparation that is constant and consistently more accurate than the Draize Test. However, scientists do not like using it. They are reluctant to abandon their old habits.

Scientific argument number 7: Better, safer and more effective alternatives are available for testing drugs.

By the end of the century doctors and scientists will look back and laugh at today's laboratories where animal experiments are used to try and test new drugs and new surgical procedures. Instead of testing drugs and chemicals on mice and rabbits, scientists will use human cells grown in the laboratory and a range of other testing facilities. The danger involved in relying on animal experiments has been so obvious that for many years sensible researchers have been looking for realistic alternatives. And they have found them.

Cell and tissue cultures

To create a cell culture individual human cells taken from diagnostic biopsies or from pieces of tissue removed during surgical procedures are grown on a culture dish or in a test tube and are covered with liquid which provides them with the 'food' they need in order to survive. To create an organ culture tiny fragments taken from a human organ are kept alive in a similar way.

Once a human cell or organ culture has been prepared – whether from the heart, kidney, liver, brain, nerves, skin or any other part of the body – drugs and other chemicals can be tested on it with remarkable speed and accuracy. Because it is possible to keep parts of virtually any organ of the body alive in this way the effectiveness of any drug or chemical can be tested with remarkable efficiency and accuracy.

Cultures of this type are exceedingly sensitive and are already being widely used in medical research to study infections, to find out more about the way anaesthetics work and to study the likely impact of chemicals and drugs on human bodies. Vast amounts of useful information about human organs and about new and existing drugs have already come from such laboratory experiments, and organizations have found them infinitely more useful, adaptable and reliable than animal experiments.

Back in 1976, for example, the World Health Organization gave its approval for the use of cell cultures to replace mice during the production of yellow fever vaccine, while drug companies who have made the financial and intellectual effort needed to switch over to culture testing have found that they can test far more substances than they ever could when they used animals. Researchers seem united in their belief that cell cultures enable them to work more speedily and to provide better results.

Computer technology

Most of the drugs that are put onto the market these days are not really new at all. They are, instead, made up of parts taken from existing drugs. Inevitably, therefore, when a 'new' drug is launched doctors will already have a considerable amount of information about how similar products affect the patients who take them.

By feeding existing knowledge into computers it is, therefore, possible to make precise, cheap and speedy predictions about the likely consequence of giving that drug to patients.

In the end clinical tests will still have to be done on real, live patients, but there is nothing new in that and by testing products first on the computer and then on cell, tissue and organ cultures it will be possible for doctors to have a much better idea of what is likely to happen when a patient takes the drug than under the present system. I know that if I had to take a new and untried drug I would be much happier if it had been tested on a series of relevant human tissue models than if it had been given, in a quite arbitrary fashion, to a member of an entirely different species.

Modern research suggests that computer technology, still in its infancy in many ways, offers endless possibilities. For example, thirty scientists working at the Los Alamos National Laboratory in America have already designed a computer program meant to duplicate the complex physiological systems of the human body. Their computer program makes it possible for scientists to make remarkably accurate predictions and to help doctors learn about diseases and treatments. Other computer programs, when linked to videos and monitor screens, enable students to learn about anatomy and physiology in great detail.

Studying people

The vast majority of the discoveries which have helped doctors save lives have been made by observant physicians and sur-

85

geons, watching their patients, watching ordinary people at work and at play and using their intelligence and their understanding of human susceptibilities to spot links between behaviour and disease.

The first firm and formally recognized association between work and disease was made in the sixteenth century by Aureolus Theophrastus Bombastus von Hohenheim (known to his friends and enemies as Paracelsus) who wrote about the relationship between mining and disease. At about the same time George Bauer published a set of twelve books which listed in some detail the type of diseases and accidents which most commonly affect miners, together with advice on how these disorders could best be avoided by the use of ventilating machines to replace stagnant air and masks to keep out mineral dust.

The official father of industrial medicine is Bernardino Ramazzini, who was a Professor of Medicine first at the University of Modena and then at Padua in the late seventeenth and early eighteenth century. While living in Modena, which at the time contained a large number of tall, overcrowded houses, Ramazzini watched a man clear out a cesspit and realized that some occupations must surely be associated with their own specific health hazards.

Inspired by this thought Ramazzini visited local mines, shops and factories and studied the type of work being done by miners, bakers, grooms, printers, blacksmiths and other labourers and craftsmen. As a direct result of his observations he was able to make specific recommendations on how work-related illnesses could best be avoided.

In 1775 the first link between chemicals and cancer was made by Percival Pott, who noticed that scrotal cancer was much more common among chimney sweeps. A few years later Thomas Beddoes reported that brassworkers and stone cutters seemed particularly susceptible to consumption.

These valuable breakthroughs promised much for medicine but over the years preventive medicine became more and more of a medical backwater as increasing numbers of doctors began to earn their living not by keeping their patients healthy, but simply by providing treatments when patients fell ill. This simple economic factor was, together with the research establishment's long-lived love affair with animal experiments, a major reason for the fact that the science of epidemiology fell into disuse. Throughout much of the nineteenth century and the first two-thirds of the twentieth century doctors were encouraged to believe that laboratories would provide them with all the answers they needed and that there was no need for them to waste time keeping their eyes open for disease.

During the 1960s things changed again, however, and during the last thirty years an enormous amount of valuable evidence has been accumulated by doctors who have studied people's habits and behavioural patterns. Today we know how four out of five cases of cancer have been caused and how most cases of heart disease have developed. Properly used this knowledge would enable doctors to prevent millions of unnecessary deaths and a tremendous amount of unnecessary pain and suffering. Observing healthy people and observing patients carefully will both provide information that could be used to combat diseases effectively.

Serendipity

Scientists do not like to think of major discoveries being made by chance, but the fact is that they frequently are, although in every case the vital factor is that the scientist who made the observation will have been alert and observant.

Take X-rays, for example, which were discovered by a fifty year old Professor of Physics called Wilhelm Konrad von Röntgen in 1895.

Röntgen was an experimental physicist working in Würzburg in Germany and in 1895 he was investigating the effects of cathode rays. What had caught Röntgen's attention was the fact that although the tube he was working with was covered with black cardboard, a greenish glow seemed to come from a piece of paper covered with a substance called barium platino-cyanide which happened to be lying on a nearby bench. Many researchers would just have moved the piece of paper, but Röntgen realized that the paper must have been made luminous by some unknown rays – something other than the cathode rays he had started off intending to investigate.

Fortunately for many millions of patients Röntgen decided to investigate further. He put a thousand page textbook between the tube and his piece of coated paper and found that the paper still became luminous. Next he placed his own hand between the tube and the piece of paper and discovered what he called X-rays when the bones of his hand, which were obviously dense enough to prevent the flow of these unseen rays, appeared on the luminous paper as dark shadows.

Within a remarkably short time specialist X-ray equipment was being made and installed in hospitals all around the world and Röntgen's discovery had revolutionized medicine and surgery in a way that few other discoveries ever have.

Countless other major discoveries have been made in the same way – with chance playing a major part in the discovery but the scientists' intelligence and natural powers of observation and curiosity playing a vital part. So, for example, Alexander Fleming was working in his laboratory at St Mary's Hospital in London in 1928 when he noticed that a culture dish containing the staphylococcus bacteria appeared to have been contaminated. The contaminant had in some way stopped the growth of the bacteria.

Contamination is a common problem in laboratories and normally such cultures are simply thrown away; but Fleming, like Röntgen, was too good a scientist to just toss away the dish and forget about it. He made careful notes and a year later published a scientific paper describing the way in which the growing spores (which he had identified as being those of penicillin) had contaminated the culture dish and prevented the growth of the bacteria.

There have been no discoveries of that significance made in recent years (whether deliberately or by chance), but many of the most useful discoveries about drugs have been made by chance. For example, drugs now widely used in the treatment of high blood pressure, epilepsy, gout and depression were 'discovered' by accident while being used for other purposes.

Excessive animal testing discourages serendipity and encourages sloppy and imprecise thinking. Animal experiments are so unreliable and so unpredictable that chance observations are not even worth recording.

Scientific argument number 8: The present system has failed. We need something new.

Whenever doctors go on strike the number of people dying falls. During a strike among hospital doctors in Israel, admissions to hospitals fell by 85 per cent and the death rate for the country dropped by 50 per cent – the largest decrease since the previous doctors' strike twenty years earlier. In 1976 doctors in Bogota, Colombia, went on strike for fifty-two days and there was a 35 per cent fall in the mortality rate. Also in 1976 a doctors' strike in Los Angeles meant that there were 60 per cent fewer operations in seventeen major hospitals. While the strike continued there was an 18 per cent reduction in the death rate. After the strike was over the death rate returned to normal.

In America there is one doctor for every 452 people and one hospital bed for every 173 people. Life expectancy there for white males is 71.8 years and for black males 65.5 years. In Switzerland there is one doctor for every 816 individuals and one hospital bed for every 177 people. The average life expectancy for males is 72.7 years. In France there is one doctor for every 480 people and one hospital bed for every 109 people. Life expectancy for males is 70.2 years. In just about every other so-called developed country the figures are similar.

Compare those figures to the figures in Jamaica, a relatively undeveloped country. In Jamaica there is one doctor for every 7,033 people and one hospital bed for every 360 prospective patients. Life expectancy for men is 69.2 years.

Or look at the figures for Korea. In North Korea there is one doctor for every 417 patients and one hospital bed for every 77 prospective patients. Life expectancy there for males is 63 years. In South Korea there is one doctor for ever 1,509 people and one hospital bed for every 676 prospective patients. Life expectancy for males is 64.9 years.

It is clear from all these figures that life expectancy (the most critical and objective way of assessing a nation's health) does not depend on the number of doctors in the country. Nor, incidentally, is there any correlation between life expectancy and the number of hospital beds.

The only possible conclusion from all this is that modern medicine is, in many ways, a failure.

The medical establishment likes to pretend that we are all living longer, healthier lives. But that is not true. A careful study of the figures shows that in most developed countries life expectancy for adults is hardly any better now than it was half a century ago; for most of this century only the dramatic reduction in infant deaths brought about by better sanitation, better housing, better water supplies and better food have helped produce figures which (superficially at least) support the establishment's argument.

Medicine has become full of confusions and paradoxes. The expenditure on health care has rocketed but the figures show that people are now more likely to fall ill than they were a generation ago. We now spend more than ever on medical research. But D. F. Horrobin of the Clinical Research Institute in Montréal, Canada, has pointed out that 'in the very few areas where advances have been made, the work was begun well before 1958'. We spend more than ever on health care but no one could argue that there is any less suffering in our society. The number of doctors goes up. But the evidence shows that people are more dissatisfied with their doctors than ever before. There is a widely held opinion among those whose job it is to assess the benefits of health care that the net value of modern medicine may be negative – in other words that over-treatment, bad treatment and abuse of technology mean that doctors do more harm than good.

It is widely agreed that 80 per cent of patients visiting a doctor need no treatment. But it is also widely acknowledged that about 80 per cent of people visiting a doctor will be given treatment. Every year doctors write out tens of millions of prescriptions for drugs which will frequently do more harm than good. In 1986 Dr Gareth Beevers, a physician at the Dudley Road Hospital in Birmingham, England, and a lecturer in medicine at Birmingham University, estimated that 10 to 15 per cent of patients are in hospital with drug-related problems.

It has been estimated that probably only one quarter of all prescriptions are necessary. So many prescriptions for commonly used drugs – antibiotics, painkillers, antacids, cough medicines, sleeping tablets, tranquillizers, vitamins and so on – are unnecessary that I doubt if I am the only doctor to believe that three quarters of all prescriptions signed by doctors are unnecessary. Around 80 per cent of the people who go to see a doctor have nothing wrong with them that would not get better with a good holiday, a lottery win or a little friendship and understanding. People want doctors they can talk to and trust. They want guidance, support, kindness and caring. But they get drugs. They get more and more dangerous and painful investigations. And they get ever more inhuman treatment. The despair and disappointment have led millions to turn to alternative practitioners.

We have specialist coronary care units for heart attack victims and more cardiologists than ever before. And yet more people than ever are dying of heart disease. And a considerable amount of evidence shows that a man or woman who has a heart attack will be better off staying at home than going into hospital.

We have been misled into thinking that we are healthier than our ancestors and that in health terms we have never had it so good. In fact the truth is very different. The truth is that our society is becoming sicker and sicker every year. Figures published by the United States Bureau of Census show that 33 per cent of people born in 1907 could expect to live to the age of seventy-five, whereas 33 per cent of the people born in 1977 could expect to live to the age of eighty. Hardly a great difference. There has, indeed, been an increase in mortality rates among the middle aged and an increase in the incidence of disabling disorders such as diabetes and arthritis. The death rate of workmen over fifty years of age was higher in the 1970s than it was in the 1930s. The British were never healthier than they were during the Second World War.

Our obsession with high technology medicine is obscene but it is spreading rapidly to underdeveloped countries. Today, in countries where the biggest cause of death is malnutrition and where the primary needs are for clean water and efficient sewage systems and more good food, extravagantly equipped surgical sites are being built and international companies are selling potentially dangerous drugs by the lorry load.

The savage truth is that today there is a huge industry which is dedicated to making people ill by producing tobacco, fatty foods and alcohol, and a huge industry making sick people sicker by giving them drugs that have never been properly tested.

The idea of testing drugs and procedures on animals is to help improve the quality of modern medicine and to improve the ability of doctors to treat and cure the sick. But all the evidence shows that doctors are, too often, making people sick rather than well. Animal research is helping to divert us from the real solutions to our problems and is largely responsible for many of our current health problems.

92

Since 1876, when the Cruelty to Animals Act was passed in the United Kingdom, over 170 million animals have been sacrificed in Britain but these experiments have done nothing to help us combat disease.

While the problems of the world continue to get worse the obsession with animal experiments continues. Every year more and more animals are used; every year more and more misleading results are obtained; and every year more and more patients suffer.

Instead of fiddling while Rome burns, today's leaders are bent over their laboratory benches apparently unaware that the world's health problem can be solved without sacrificing an endless stream of animals; apparently unaware that their grotesque procedures are killing patients as well as animals.

5 | WHY ANIMAL EXPERIMENTS CONTINUE

IF THE EVIDENCE AGAINST VIVISECTION is so powerful why do so many people still perform – or support – animal experiments? The answer is simple: there are powerful vested interests involved. And the bottom line is money.

The thousands of people who still perform animal experiments do so because that is the way they earn their living. They do not know how to do anything else and most of them lack the intelligence to learn new skills. The many individuals whose careers are built upon animal experimentation are as dependent upon animals, and as reluctant to accept any suggested changes in what they do, as are the thousands of individuals who earn their living from breeding, farming, capturing and selling laboratory animals or from devising and selling animal restraints or cages. The drug companies and the university departments which sponsor and protect the experiments are desperate to protect their investments, because they know that animal experiments can be done cheaply and can be used to generate massive profits. Moreover, they know that to change the ways in which things are done will cost a lot of money.

None of these individuals or organizations are prepared to admit that animal experiments are of no value, because if they do then their past work will be discredited, their academic achievements will be permanently devalued and the products which they have marketed will probably have to be re-tested or withdrawn. Moreover, they will know that their lives will have been wasted on useless and morally inexcusable and indefensible work. Researchers and those who employ them have a powerful vested interest in maintaining the status quo and in resisting attempts to introduce new technologies.

When you remember that animal researchers are fighting for their professional reputations and their financial security, it is hardly surprising that they should lie and deceive. When you remember that companies and other organizations are fighting for their present and future profits, it is hardly surprising that they are prepared to spend large sums of money protecting themselves.

Here are just a few specific examples of ways in which people have benefited from animal experiments (I have not included specific researchers who have obtained fat grants or specific drug companies which have made money by selling drugs tested on animals):

● An American mouse-breeding firm has for some time been selling genetically engineered mice for one hundred dollars each. The mice being sold were virtually guaranteed to develop cancer within ninety days and to die soon afterwards. The company has protected its investment with a patent.

● A maker of laboratory equipment has devised an individual water dispenser which is programmed to deliver an electric shock each time an animal takes a drink from it. The aim is to make the animal so anxious that it eventually stops drinking. To heighten the efficiency of the device experimenters are advised to deprive animals of water for two days before putting them into the tiny cage to which the water dispenser is attached.

● Another company offers for sale a treadmill with variable speed controls and an adjustable device for giving electric shocks. The basic system costs around £10,000. The de luxe model (which automatically monitors the time the animal spends on the treadmill and the amount of time it spends being given electric shocks) costs more.

● Another scientist (who probably prefers to remain anonymous) invented a machine capable of hitting dogs' hind legs 225 times a minute.

Those are just a very small selection of the thousands of people and companies who have, between them, created careers and fortunes out of experiments on animals.

But there are other, even more worrying reasons why animal experiments continue.

First, young scientists know that if they object to animal experiments they are likely to find their careers in ruins. The power of the establishment is vast and, as Dr E. J. H. Moore pointed out in *The Lancet* a few years ago, 'young doctors must say nothing, at least in public, about the abuse of laboratory animals, for fear of jeopardizing their career prospects'. Scientists and doctors who have been brave enough to speak out and attempt to get things changed have quickly learned just how vicious a threatened establishment can be.

The second reason why animal experiments continue is that they are wonderfully flexible. As I have already shown (see pages 51 to 52) they can be used to justify the launch of a new product, but they can also be rejected and abandoned as irrelevant if anything disastrous should happen when the new product is given to human patients. Paradoxically, the very unreliability of animal experiments can be one of their main benefits as far as drug companies are concerned. Tobacco companies have made huge amounts of money out of the fact that misleading and pointless animal experiments enabled them to create confusion and uncertainty about the link between cigarette smoking and the development of cancer.

Researchers also use the unreliability of animal experiments to help them launch over-optimistic fund raising schemes. So, for example, if a new drug proves to be of value in treating a particular type of cancer in a rare or especially bred strain of mice, the charity or institution which has sponsored the research will use the results to justify public appeals for extra money. The extravagant claims and talk about 'breakthroughs' will be tempered by a small print warning that the drug is still at the experimental stage. But if the publicity has been carefully designed the results will bring in vast quantities of money from people who are dying, whose relatives are dying or who are frightened of dying but unwilling to change their own bad habits.

Finally, and perhaps most worrying of all, there is the fact that the medical establishment – led by doctors and drug companies – undoubtedly relies upon animal experiments to help keep offering patients hope and, therefore, to help put off the day when orthodox medical practices will be at least partly replaced by safer and more effective alternatives.

Light bulb manufacturers have a vested interest in light bulbs burning out quickly. Motor car manufacturers have a vested interest in cars falling apart through rust. And drug companies and doctors stand to lose vast amounts of money if people ever truly learn the secret of good health. Drug companies do not really want people to get better. They make far more money out of drugs which are designed to alleviate symptoms such as pain than they would if they were selling products which cured diseases. And they stand to make nothing at all out of advice which successfully prevents disease. In my book *Bodypower* I described how patients can successfully treat at least

98

90 per cent of all illnesses without any medical intervention. The book has been translated into a dozen languages and has been a bestseller all around the world, but no doctor has ever successfully opposed the theme of the book: indeed, when questioned doctors have had to admit that the principles outlined in the book are all completely accurate.

Doctors and drug companies earn their living out of selling drugs. They need to maintain the status quo. If animal experiments were abandoned the constant stream of new drugs would be slowed to a trickle, since preliminary tests would have to be done in a more reliable way and the majority of new drugs would never be granted licences for general use. Within a few years most of the world's largest drug companies would be bankrupt and countless thousands of doctors would be unemployed. The vast majority of doctors earn the major portion of their incomes from prescribing remedies for symptoms; very few earn any money from offering practical advice to patients on how to stay healthy. The doctors who earn a living out of selling so-called cures know that if their cures were genuinely effective they would soon be put out of business. Studying diseases, and performing unreliable and unpredictable animal experiments, enables the profession (and the drug industry) to keep on making money.

6 WHAT YOU CAN DO TO HELP STOP ANIMAL EXPERIMENTS

ANIMAL EXPERIMENTS ARE PERFORMED with your money and on your behalf. You have a right to make your voice heard. And you can be more powerful than you think. In the end public opinion will prevail and animal experiments will be stopped.

Virtually all animal experiments are performed either with your money or on your behalf. You have a right to complain, a right to state your opinion and a right to expect people to listen to you. The system which supports and protects animal experimentation is endangering your health, your family's health and the health of your friends and neighbours, and the people who defend animal experimentation do so because they have a vested personal interest in ensuring that nothing changes.

I have prepared below a simple 10-point plan to help show you exactly how you can ensure that your voice is heard.

1. Do not allow yourself to be frightened or intimidated by

101

claims made by eminent sounding doctors and scientists. Some of the most reputable looking and best established doctors and scientists are remarkably low on intelligence, and integrity. Anyone – however important sounding – who claims that animal experiments are valuable and essential is either a fool or a liar. Read as many books on the subject as you can, but always treat scientific dogmatism with caution and scepticism. (In response to critics who might claim that I am being dogmatic I would point out that I would encourage readers of this book to read as much as they can on the subject of animal experimentation – including literature written and published by those who support vivisection.) Always make so-called experts substantiate and explain their claims and never stop asking embarrassing questions like 'Why?' and 'So what?'

2. Join at least one anti-vivisection group and read the literature they produce. You will, inevitably, find that there is a tremendous difference between the quality of literature available: some is distinctly amateurish, while other publications are highly professional. Attend meetings when you can and learn as much as possible about a group's motives and achievements before giving money. As an alternative to giving money directly consider buying books, leaflets or pamphlets (or even producing your own) and then giving or sending copies to people who you think you may be able to influence. You will undoubtedly find that many of the people you try to convert will have been successfully brain-washed by the standard 'this rat or your child' argument. Be patient with them and be prepared for the fact that they may find it exceedingly difficult to accept that spokesmen for the medical establishment have been lying.

3. Before giving any money to any charity find out as much as you can about how your money will be spent. A surprisingly large number of medically based charities use their funds to pay for animal experiments. If you are in any doubt ask the charity's representatives to tell you whether or not they ever pay for animal experiments. If they admit that they do they will almost certainly claim that only relevant and useful experiments are performed. Because you know the truth you will be able to explain that you will give them money only when they stop supporting pointless and barbaric experiments. You may be able to persuade them to re-think their funding programmes. As a general rule try to give money to charities which help people or animals directly rather than 'helping' by supporting or subsidizing useless research projects.

4. Complain to your political representatives, but do make sure that any literature you send is easy to read and free of extravagant graphics. The feedback from politicians is often discouraging but do keep at it. Although they may be reluctant to argue with the official establishment line, good, wary politicians are always quick to react when they realize that a particular line of attack may attract popular support and further their own careers.

5. Try to buy personal and household products which have not been tested on animals. Many anti-vivisection groups now publish lists of toiletries, medicines and chemicals which have not been tested on animals. If you find that you have no choice but to buy a product that has been tested on animals, write a polite but firm letter of complaint to the shop and the manufacturer. Several major international cosmetics companies have changed their policy about experimenting on animals because of protests from customers. If you find a company that insists on continuing with animal tests, write and tell the chairman why you are not buying his company's products; write to the company's suppliers and distributors and complain; buy one share and turn up at the company's Annual General Meeting and ask the chairman why his company persists with useless animal testing; and encourage other shoppers to boycott the company's products and to boycott newspapers, magazines and television stations which carry advertizing for any of the company's products.

6. Send letters of protest to newspapers, magazines and radio and television stations if you feel that they have carried misleading items about the value of animal experiments. In addition, if you become aware of information which you think might make a good news story ring up the news editor. When talking to journalists always try to differentiate between facts and opinions. Do not, however, be too upset if at first you find it difficult to generate supportive publicity. Drug companies, universities and members of the medical establishment have a lot of money and a lot of commercial 'clout' and many apparently independent reporters and TV or radio presenters will be worried about upsetting establishment figures.

You may find that you are mocked or belittled, but however enraged you may be by the lies told by your opponents, try not to lose your temper. (I have been falsely described as a Nazi and as a communist; wrongly accused of having been struck off the medical register; and one scientist accused me of making up the things I had accused him of even though I had always been careful to quote his work from his own published scientific papers.) If you stay calm the audience will be more likely to sympathize with you and support you. Do remember, however, that because your opponents do not want the subject aired at all (since any publicity is always bound to be bad for the status quo and since they cannot win anything but could lose something) you should be grateful for any publicity you can get.

Even if an article or broadcast only persuades one individual of the evils of vivisection you will have helped. To illustrate the difficulty the anti-vivisection movement has in obtaining coverage, I would mention that after I was made President of LIMAV (Ligue Internationale Médicins pour l'Abolition de la Vivisection) a press release pointing out that 572 doctors from twenty-eight countries had joined together to argue that animal experiments were so misleading that they were a health hazard was sent to a large number of medical journals. None of them carried any details about LIMAV, though in the week that it might have been expected to carry the story the *British Medical Journal* did manage to find space for details of a seminar offering doctors working for the National Health Service advice on how to claim removal expenses from their employers.

7. Try to convince your doctors that animal experiments are making their life more difficult by allowing drug companies to market drugs which are not properly tested before being sold. Once you have convinced them of the truth, suggest that they tell drug company representatives that they would rather prescribe drugs that have not been tested on animals.

8. If you are a student and your teachers expect you to perform vivisection experiments, you have a right to protest and to refuse to take any part in animal experiments. Millions of animals are used each year in schools and colleges, but most good educational establishments now allow students to opt out of vivisection experiments without any penalties – although some rather outdated and unthinking lecturers still believe that students should be forced to chop up animals.

Writing in the *British Medical Journal* recently one commentator (hiding behind a pen name) suggested that because many science students are now allowed to choose alternatives to dissection students may choose to study other subjects. I suspect that the truth is that far more students are likely to be put off science by the thought that they are expected to perform cruel and entirely pointless experiments on animals. To suggest that students cannot possibly understand human life without chopping up rats or frogs is as absurd as claiming that students cannot possibly understand geography without travelling around the world or cannot understand history without travelling backwards through time. There is real sadness in the thought that

105

some people still think that students will not be attracted to 'life' sciences unless they can chop up dead animals.

It is, I think, worth pointing out that in 1987 the Argentinian government banned dissection in schools and stated that 'biology is the science of life and it is not consistent to teach it at the expense of other beings'. The Argentinian government also pointed out that 'experiments on animals are part of a dangerous process which tends to desensitize the mind to pain and suffering'. In some American states laws have been passed requiring schools to provide alternatives for students who object to dissecting animals – whether live or dead.

9. Be aware of the fact that it is not just the drug and chemical companies that test their products on animals. Many food additives are tested on animals (so whenever possible buy organically grown food); furs, wool, leather and cotton are all turned into clothes with the aid of chemicals tested on animals and manmade fibres are also prepared with similar chemicals (so buy as few clothes as possible and use your clothes until they wear out); many household and garden products are tested on animals (so try not to buy products that are described as 'new' or 'improved' or are said to contain ingredients that are 'more powerful than ever').

10. If you become an active member of almost any antivivisection group you will, I'm afraid, quickly become aware of the sad fact that anti-vivisectionists are often their own very worst enemies.

Over the years I have become painfully conscious of the fact that many of the organizations and individuals who claim to oppose the use of animals in experiments spend most of their energies in fighting one another instead of fighting for animals.

There are bound to be disagreements about style and method of attack. There are bound to be disagreements about how far anti-vivisectionists should go in criticizing those who perform animal experiments. There are bound to be variations in the aims of campaigners too; some anti-vivisectionists believe that some animal experiments can be justified.

All these variations are natural and inevitable within a massive international movement that involves millions of committed individuals.

But there is no justification for the sort of internecine warfare which exists within the anti-vivisectionist movement.

Vivisectors never disagree in public. Mad scientists never say anything uncomplimentary about one another. They do not waste their time or their energies on squabbling. My personal feeling is that it does not matter one jot whether other anti-vivisectionists agree or disagree with my own style of attack. And I refuse to be angered by the knowledge that many anti-vivisectionists are content to argue only that *some* experiments should be stopped.

The important thing is that we are all campaigning in the same direction. I would not be especially keen to join a society which said that animal experiments should only be banned on Saturdays and Sundays, but I would not actively oppose such a society. I would not have too much respect for a society which said only that scientists whose names began with K should not be allowed to do experiments. But what would be the point in attacking such societies? Their aims and mine might differ, but at least we would all be aiming in the same general direction. I would rather spend my time attacking vivisectors and fighting to stop animal experiments than in attacking other people whose views differ in relatively minor ways from mine.

I believe that those of us who oppose animal experiments should work together. We should welcome anyone who agrees with our general aims and resist the temptation ever to judge or condemn those whose methods or aims might differ slightly from our own. We have a big enough fight on our hands without making things harder by fighting one another.

107

We vivisect the nightingale
To probe the secret of his note

T. B. ALDRICH (1836–1907)

Also published by the European Medical Journal

Betrayal of Trust

Vernon Coleman

Betrayal of Trust follows in the tradition of Vernon Coleman's most iconoclastic and ground-breaking books—*The Medicine Men, Paper Doctors,* and *The Health Scandal.*

Dr Coleman catalogues the incompetence and dishonesty of the medical profession and the pharmaceutical industry and explains the historical background to the problems which exist today. He shows how drugs are put onto the market without being properly tested, and provides hard evidence for his astonishing assertion that doctors now do more harm than good.

To support his claim that drug companies use animal tests to get their drugs on the market, Dr Coleman lists scores of widely prescribed drugs which are reguarly prescribed for patients, despite the fact that there is evidence showing that the drugs cause serious problems when given to animals.

Drug companies are, he explains, in a 'no lose' situation. If a new drug seems safe when given to animals, the company making it uses that evidence to help get the drug a licence. But if a new drug causes problems when given to animals, that evidence is ignored as irrelevant! Only patients lose.

"When animal experiments are stopped," says Dr Coleman, "they will never be reintroduced. The moral, ethical, scientific and medical evidence all supports the contention that animal experiments must be stopped now."

ISBN 0 9521492 2 2 160pp

ALL ROYALTIES AND PROCEEDS GO TO HELP THE FIGHT AGAINST ANIMAL EXPERIMENTATION

Available from Book Sales, European Medical Journal, Lynmouth, Devon EX35 6EE, UK.
Please write for catalogue.

Also published by the European Medical Journal

Know Your Drugs
Vernon Coleman

In addition to containing basic information—including side effects—about more than 100 of the most commonly prescribed prescription drugs, *Know Your Drugs* also includes:

- Tips for taking a prescription drug
- Common side effects
- How to read your prescription
- Ways to tell if your doctor is trying out a new drug on you
- Drugs which were so dangerous they had to be banned
- The top ten prescription groups
- Why you might have to take drugs for the rest of your life
- Questions to ask your doctor before taking a drug
- Drugs that are useless
- Tips for patients taking antibiotics
- Side effects which are common among elderly patients
- Why pregnant women should take care with drugs
- Tips for patients coming off tranquillisers
- Tips for women on the contraceptive pill
- Don't take pills indefinitely!

ISBN 0 9521492 5 7
160pp paperback

ALL ROYALTIES AND PROCEEDS GO TO HELP THE FIGHT
AGAINST ANIMAL EXPERIMENTATION.

Available from:
Book Sales, European Medical Journal,
Lynmouth, Devon EX35 6EE, UK.
Please write for catalogue.

Also published by the European Medical Journal

Food for Thought
The European Medical Association's Healthy Eating Report
Vernon Coleman

Packed with easy-to-use, up to date, practical information, *Food for Thought* is designed to help you differentiate between fact and fantasy when planning your diet. The book's 28 chapters include:

- Food the fuel: basic information about carbohydrates, protein, fat, vitamins and minerals
- When water isn't safe to drink—and what to do about it
- How what you eat affects your health
- Why snacking is good for you
- The mini-meal diet and the painless way to lose weight
- Quick tips for losing weight
- The Thirty-Nine Steps to Slenderness
- 20 magic superfoods that can improve your health
- The harm food additives can do
- 20-point plan for avoiding food poisoning
- Drugs and hormones in food
- Food irradiation, genetically altered food, microwaves
- 30 common diseases—and their relationship to what you eat
- How to eat a healthy diet
- 21 reasons for being a vegetarian
- How much should you weigh?
- How to deal with children who are overweight

ISBN 0 9521492 6 5 192pp paperback

ALL ROYALTIES AND PROCEEDS GO TO HELP THE FIGHT AGAINST ANIMAL EXPERIMENTATION.

Available from:
Book Sales, European Medical Journal, Lynmouth,
Devon EX35 6EE, UK.
Please write for catalogue.